Human Aspects of Police Driving

Gordon R Sharp MD, PhD, FRCP(Glas), FFOM, RAF(Retd)

Contents

The Scottish Police College would like to thank Volvo Car UK Limited for their assistance in the production and promotion of this publication.

Foreword

The recording of UK injury road accident statistics began in 1926. Analysis of these figures has progressively identified that the most significant, single contributory factor in the overwhelming majority of road accidents is the 'human factor', otherwise known as 'driver error'.

It is argued that basic driving skills can be enhanced in order to reduce the likelihood of accidents. For instance, between the mid 1930's and the mid 1990's police vehicle accident records point to a reduction in the blameworthy accident rate from one accident in every eight thousand miles travelled to one for almost every quarter of a million miles covered. This period happens to coincide with the introduction and spread of police advanced driver training. While it is recognised that other factors will have undoubtedly aided in this spectacular reduction, few would, I think, argue against the contribution that "System Driving" has made.

The fact remains though, that even highly trained and skilled police advanced drivers occasionally make mistakes leading to accidents. Why does that happen? What can cause a driver to make the wrong decisions? What factors influence the overriding of previously ingrained good practice? Why are the capabilities of the vehicle, combined with existing road, weather and traffic conditions, sometimes ignored or exceeded?

In the absence of vehicle or road defects, the 'human factor' must surely be a key contributor, a factor which has promoted an examination of the processes by which external and internal influences affect decision making during an emergency driving event.

This book explores this vital area and aims to provide a better understanding of how our minds are influenced, and perhaps our personal control mechanisms overtaken, in the course of our involvement in such incidents. Through an improved appreciation of our inherent human frailties, we can perhaps begin to mitigate the effects of negative influences and prevent the potentially disastrous consequences which can result.

While written predominantly for the traffic patrol officer, the contents will, I think, prove invaluable reading for all those involved in police operational driving, advanced driver training and for our driver colleagues in the other emergency services. I believe that its publication contributes to the advancement of attitudinal training carried out at all police driver training establishments throughout the United Kingdom and beyond.

My sincere thanks go to Dr Gordon Sharp for the gift of his expertise, his professionalism, enthusiasm and wholehearted commitment to the safety of our officers and to that of the public which they serve.

Hugh I Watson OBE QPM
Commandant
The Scottish Police College

Preface

As an Occupational Physician, the Author has long been fascinated by the interactions between the human body, the workplace and the performance of tasks. The idea of writing a book on the work of Police Drivers originated during early research studies conducted on Emergency Service Crews responding to road traffic accidents. The results of medical, physiological, psychological and ergonomic observations indicated that many of the human reactions encountered during those difficult and demanding operations were similar in many aspects to those found in high performance military flying—a field of research in which the Author has been deeply involved for many years.

Using techniques originally developed for Aerospace Medical Research, further investigations were directed towards studies of the human aspects of a Rapid Response and Fast Pursuit during Police Operations. The findings of this project led to the inclusion of Attitude Development and Human Aspects Training in Advanced Driving Courses, first at the Scottish Police College and later in those conducted by other Police Driving Schools throughout the United Kingdom.

This book is intended primarily to act as a reference companion to the Roadcraft Manual which is the standard work used by Police Drivers attending Advanced Driving Courses. Much of the information contained within its Chapters has been gleaned from the Author's own observations and investigations and draws on research carried out by many experts in their field. Until now little of that knowledge has been available to Police Drivers in a form designed especially for them and this book sets out to remedy this situation. It presents the material in an essentially practical way, does not purport to deal with the subject exhaustively, and deliberately avoids detailed and highly scientific explanations. It is aimed principally at the requirements of Traffic Police Officers but it is hoped that it will be useful to members of the other Emergency Services as well as motorists who wish to obtain a greater understanding of how the human mind and body react in a man-machine environment.

A word of apology must be made to all female readers for the fact that the Driver is referred to as "he" throughout the Chapters. This is merely to avoid the cumbersome and repetitive use of "he/she" and the Author fully recognises that more and more female Police Officers join their male colleagues amongst the driving elite.

Acknowledgements and Dedication

Acknowledgements
The Author would like to express his appreciation of the generous support given by the Commandant and Staff of the Scottish Police College and by Chief Inspector Andrew Bright and members of staff of the Traffic Training Division for the great assistance given by them in the preparation of this book. Special thanks are due to the Chief Superintendent Traffic and Operational Support Services, Central Scotland Police, for permission to conduct on-board patrol vehicle studies and to the many Traffic Patrol Officers who so willingly and unselfishly participated in these investigations.

Thanks also go to the Chairman of the Forth Valley Health Board for support and encouragement during the conduct of the "Preventative Medicine Programme" from which many of the observations used in this book have been derived.

It is a pleasure to acknowledge the assistance given by Chief Inspector Jack Ramsay and staff of the Support Services Division of the Scottish Police College, in the publication of this book.

Photographs have been reproduced by the kind permission of the following organisations—Figure 3.2 is from "Hospital Doctor"; Figure 10.2 is from Cleveland Constabulary and Figures 4.1 and 12.1 are included by courtesy of "SHOUT".

Finally, sincere thanks are due to Mrs Margaret Smith for her great assistance and untiring efforts in the organisation and preparation of text and other materials used in the book.

This project has been funded in part by the OccuMedic Research Foundation.

Dedication
It is the Author's hope that the information presented in the following Chapters may assist the efforts of many people and organisations who are working tirelessly to improve standards of driving and road safety. To all of them this book is gladly dedicated.

Gordon R Sharp

Chapter 1
Advanced Driving Skills

Introduction

The work of the Traffic Police Officer is varied and at times difficult and dangerous. During the course of a single shift, driving operations may change from a routine patrol to a rapid response and may end up as a fast pursuit. The tasks which the driver may be required to perform are also many and varied and can change suddenly and without warning. At one moment he may be required to control heavy traffic flow on a busy motorway, and in the next attend a road traffic accident or deal with a chemical spillage from an overturned tanker. He must be prepared to apply a wide range of skills in a variety of different working environments, some of which are friendly and others decidedly hostile. Yet in all these he is expected to maintain a high standard of performance that is appropriate to every circumstance and situation.

11

Within the core task of driving the Police Officer requires not only to attain and maintain an exceptionally high degree of proficiency but also to develop specialised aspects of the skill upon which the success and possibly the safety of an operation may depend. Analysis has identified some of the specialised elements which are of particular importance in operational police driving and these are summarised as follows:—

▶ *Time Sharing*—During police operations the driver must possess the ability to carry out several complex tasks at the same time and be able to apply to each task equally high standards of accuracy and efficiency.

▶ *Attention Distribution*—In a complicated and difficult drive he must have the facility to distribute his attention over a wide range so that he can deal with all aspects of the task in a systematic and methodical manner.

▶ *Situational Awareness*—The driver must acquire a keen sense of awareness about himself, his vehicle and surroundings. He must employ all his senses to gather information and build up an accurate mental "picture" of the operational situation.

▶ *Plan Formulating*—The driver must be able to formulate precise plans of action and make accurate and rapid decisions during the most difficult and demanding phases of the drive.

▶ *Anticipation*—He must develop exceptional powers of anticipation, using his observation skills and experience to predict how a situation is likely to unfold.

▶ *Judgement Making*—He must possess keen powers of judgement so that in stressful and demanding operations his driving and other tasks are appropriate, accurate and safely executed.

▶ *Alertness*—The driver must bring to all his operational tasks a high degree of alertness, vigilance and intense concentration so that no potential hazards are missed and nothing is left to chance.

12

Like any other motor task it takes time to acquire the necessary skills for proficient driving, and considerable practice to maintain them in good working order. The Officer who wishes to achieve the highest standards of driving must concentrate on building on his existing skills, adding to them the complex manoeuvres and procedures that may be required in demanding police operations. He must also expand and refine the higher mental processes which control and direct the accuracy and safety of all his driving activities. Reaching the peak of driving perfection is therefore a continuous process of skill development which begins in the early learning phase, progresses through more advanced stages to acquiring multiple and complex advanced skills. This Chapter aims to trace the path of this learning process and to create an understanding of the many human aspects involved in the development of advanced professional driving skills.

Acquiring Motor Skills

Driving is a complex task that involves physical as well as mental activity. The physical aspects include the body movements required to start the vehicle, move off, accelerate, steer and brake, as well as the sequences needed to manoeuvre in a confined space. When he has mastered these motor skills the trained driver can carry them out in a precise co-ordinated manner which enables him to progress safely and steadily along his intended path and negotiate every hazard.

Driving Movements

It is important to understand the many different body movements involved in even the simplest operation of a vehicle control. Preliminary movements of the trunk get the body into the correct position to reach and operate the control easily and precisely. Primary movements of the arms are employed to steer the vehicle or change gear while corresponding leg movements are used to operate foot pedals like the

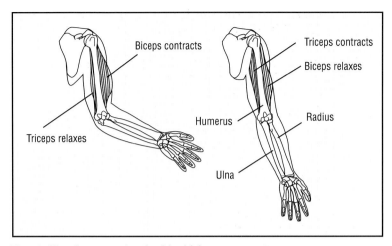

Biceps contracts

Triceps contracts

Biceps relaxes

Humerus

Radius

Triceps relaxes

Ulna

13

Fig 1.1: Muscle groups involved in driving movements

brake and clutch. Limb movements consist of a combination of pulling, pushing and turning actions coupled with finer and more precise movements of the fingers used in the operation of switches and control knobs. While these activities are taking place other ancillary movements are used to counterbalance the body and maintain the driver in a sitting posture that enables him to control his vehicle at all times.

Driving actions are brought about through the function of the body's musculoskeletal system. This comprises bones that provide the rigid structure of the skeleton and act as levers, joints and hinges for movement of various parts. The power to deliver movement comes from the muscles which are made up of bundles of elongated fibres that contract or shorten in length as a result of complex chemical processes. Muscles like those in the arm transmit their movement through fibrous tendons which connect them to bony levers. Contraction of the biceps (Figure 1.1) moves the bony lever of the arm and bends the elbow, while contraction of the opposite or antagonistic muscle (the triceps) straightens it out again. Even when the driver is not operating controls or actively moving his limbs, some muscles like those of the back, remain in a permanent state of tension in order to hold up the head, neck and trunk in an upright sitting posture. In a later Chapter the significance of postural muscle tone in the production of driver's fatigue and backache will be studied in more detail.

Co-ordination

The process by which all the individual muscle contractions are synchronized into a smooth order of activity is called co-ordination,

(Figure 1.2). Before the driver can carry out a simple control operation a series of co-ordinated events must occur. First the brain must "know" the location of the control to be operated, and the relationship between it and the driver's arm, hand and fingers. If the control position is unfamiliar, he will use his visual sense to locate it but in most cases the brain already holds a "spatial location" map built up by frequent use of that control. The brain centre checks the map to ensure that the limb has adequate space to reach and operate the control, and thereafter solves the problem of how to get the arm

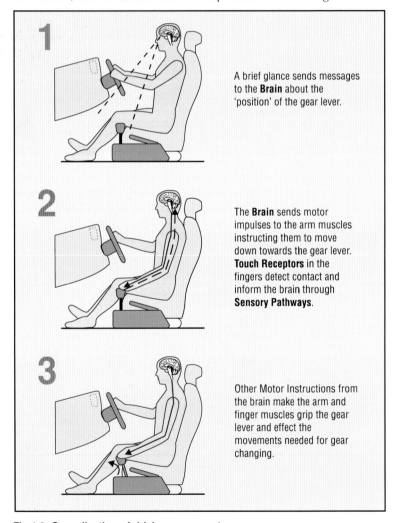

1 A brief glance sends messages to the **Brain** about the 'position' of the gear lever.

2 The **Brain** sends motor impulses to the arm muscles instructing them to move down towards the gear lever. **Touch Receptors** in the fingers detect contact and inform the brain through **Sensory Pathways**.

3 Other Motor Instructions from the brain make the arm and finger muscles grip the gear lever and effect the movements needed for gear changing.

Fig 1.2: Co-ordination of driving movements

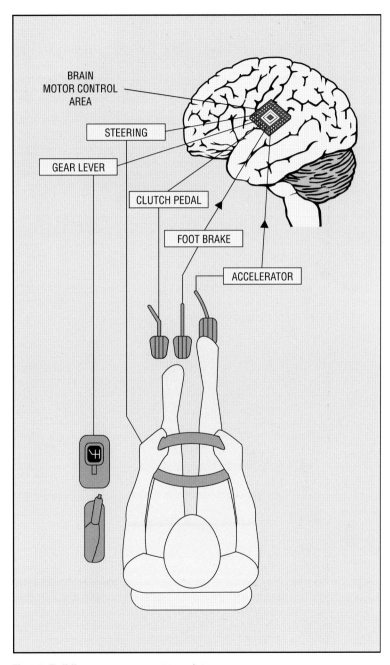

Fig 1.3: Building up a movement template

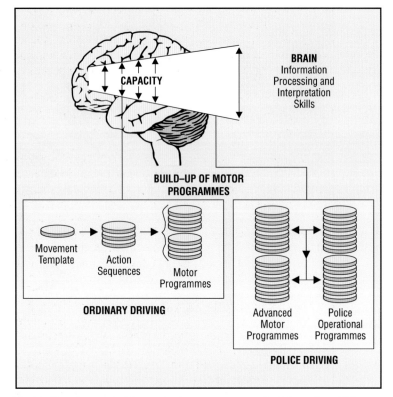

Fig 1.4: Development of the motor programmes required for police driving

and hand to it. It also calculates which ancillary movements will be needed to position the body in a way that will facilitate the control movement. When complete, the action plan is finally translated into a detailed set of instructions that go out to the muscles commanding some to contract and others to relax in a co-ordinated sequence.

Laying Down Motor Programmes

The advanced motor skills which are developed by the Police Driver are built up on those originally laid down in the early stages of driving. In these early phases the learner concentrates on the individual body movements needed to operate and control the vehicle. At first he focusses his attention on each individual skill element and as a consequence actions like gear changing, operating the clutch or brake pedals and steering all tend to be slow, deliberate and rather clumsy. With practice they become smoother as he begins to co-ordinate his muscular actions and develop reflexes that involve the brain, motor and sensory nerves.

With further practice several individual movements are combined into a sequence which becomes etched as a *movement template* into the motor control area of the brain (Figure 1.3). When the driver has reached this stage his driving actions are performed without them reaching conscious level. This allows more brain power to be directed to other aspects of driving which consequently becomes more efficient, economical of movement and considerably smoother. Eventually the conscious mind is concerned only with finding the right sequence of motor actions to suit the occasion.

With experience, individual templates are combined together and built into a library of *action sequences* laid down in the motor programme area of the brain (Figure 1.4). When a manoeuvre demands several operations such as steering, accelerating, gear changing or braking, an appropriate combined sequence like this can be called into action. More experience expands these action sequences into a collection of *motor programmes* that gives the brain a wide choice of more complicated driving manoeuvres that suit a range of all types of traffic and other conditions. As the driver continues to build up these motor programmes he simultaneously expands his *brain processing capacity* (Figure I.4) and this allows him to assess and interpret his driving situation, formulate accurate plans of action and make sound judgements. As part of Advanced Driver Training the Officer builds on the knowledge and experience which he has gained and adds even more complex manoeuvres to the existing store of motor programmes. This wider choice enables him to respond in the correct way to the most demanding operation with driving techniques that are both appropriate and safe.

Expanding Higher Mental Skills

In parallel with the acquisition of motor programmes, advancement of driving performance to Police operational standards requires development of higher mental processing abilities. These are the skill elements shown in Figure 1.5 which enable the driver to choose the most appropriate action or manoeuvre, check it for suitability and safety and monitor it throughout its operation. The main elements comprise the following:—

▶ Observation
▶ Perception
▶ Decision Making
▶ Judgement Forming
▶ Action Monitoring

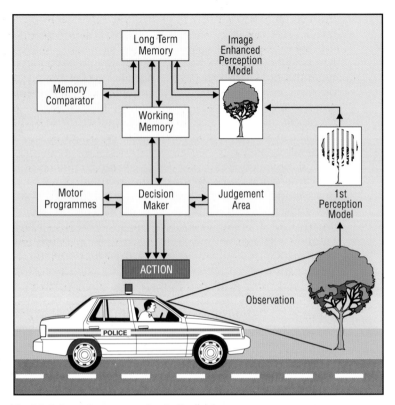

Fig 1.5: Information processing in the brain

Observation

Information processing in the brain starts with accurate observation that enables the driver to obtain details about himself, his surroundings and the progress of his vehicle. He uses his eyes to scan the road ahead looking for such things as road signs, markings and layout that will help to provide him with information about his situation. His scanning will take in items like junctions, pathways, exits and entrances alerting him to the possibility of conflicting or emerging traffic. Ruts, holes and surface water all provide further information about road conditions while observations on the position of other road users help him to anticipate their likely actions and allow him to plan his driving tactics in advance.

Although vision is the most important sense used by the driver, valuable information can be obtained from hearing through detection of changes in pitch of the engine, road surface vibration noise and warning signals from other road users. Even the sense of smell can add to an overall knowledge of the surroundings and the characteristic smell of newly cut grass can alert the driver to the possible presence of mowing machinery. Farmyard odours warn him to expect the presence of animals or agricultural vehicles on the road ahead. Similarly, sensory input signals from specialised mechano-receptors embedded in muscles, joints and tissues provide vibration and other clues about the terrain and road surface over which the vehicle is passing. The proficient driver uses every available observation clue to help him create an awareness of his surroundings and gain a better understanding of his situation. All available information is passed on to the "perception area" of the brain where it is further analysed and interpreted.

19

Perception

Using information obtained from vision and other senses, the brain builds up a "map" or "model" of the surroundings. The more detailed the observations the more accurate is the model and the greater the information which is available for decision and judgement making. An "image frame" within the model is seldom complete and lasts only a fraction of a second before it decays to be replaced by new information. The brain however uses that short time to fill in gaps and complete missing details in the same way that a television image can be enhanced. It does so by cross-referring to the "bank of images" stored in memory that have been obtained from previous experience and knowledge. When the perception model has been enhanced, the gaps filled in and it is as complete as possible, it is used for further analyses within the working memory area.

Decision Making

The process of decision making takes place within the working memory area of the brain. Here information contained in the enhanced perception model is used to formulate a plan of action and decide on suitable manoeuvres. The first process is one of comparison whereby the current image perceived by the driver is compared with frames and images stored in long-term memory from previous situations. The brain tries to make an association between the information it is currently receiving about the outside world and the data in the perception model which it has built up. It searches the image database in long-term memory and when it finds a match it goes on to seek further matches and associations from which it compiles a selection of possible actions. If reasonably close matches have been found the brain checks back again to find out what actions were taken by the driver on previous occasions, whether they were appropriate to the situation and whether they resulted in a satisfactory and safe outcome. A decision is now made whether to draw on an existing motor programme or modify another one to better suit the circumstances. The choice depends on the available range of programmed manoeuvre sequences and the ones most closely matching the situation are finally selected for use. Before the plan is brought into operation however, information is passed to the processing centre where judgements, assessments and evaluations are carried out. This is the centre in the brain known as the Judgement Forming Area.

Judgement Forming

Once the brain has decided on a potentially suitable plan of action, details are passed over to the Judgement Forming Area where an assessment is made about its suitability and whether it will meet the requirements. The power of judgement is essentially a human characteristic and the driver employs many types in the course of his driving task. Dimensional judgements are used to gauge whether there is enough room to carry out the manoeuvre and the brain calculates and cross-checks that it will be carried out with the vehicle in the correct position, travelling at the right speed and with the appropriate gear engaged.

More importantly, the judgement process involves assessing the risk of the proposed plan and this is one of the elements of information processing which police drivers must hone to perfection. It is this facility upon which the safety of the operation may depend. It begins when the brain tries to associate its present situation and the proposed plan of action with previous actions that have been carried out safely in similar circumstances. It makes these links through a process of "risk grading" whereby the judgement centre checks the perception model frame-by-frame comparing it with its store of "safe-action-situations". It notes possible sources of hazard, grades them accordingly and calculates the potential risk of these occurring during the proposed manoeuvre. This process of risk grading illustrated in Figure 1.6 shows some of the typical situations and the risk value attached to each encounter. An agricultural setting with no obvious hazard visible might be graded as low risk; a tractor just appearing in the field of view would represent a higher risk and when observed as about to pull out of an entrance, would be rated as a potential high risk for collision.

The judgement process also checks other aspects of the plan for safety noting bends in the road, hillcrests, humpback bridges or other obstructions to a clear view, adding them to the risk assessment of the proposed manoeuvre. Likewise, icy, muddy or wet roads evoke memories of previous poor road holding and will modify the risk grading accordingly.

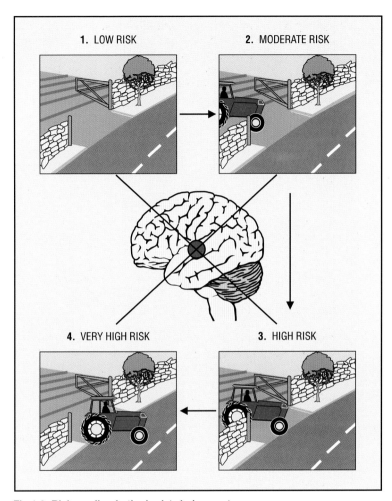

1. LOW RISK   **2. MODERATE RISK**

4. VERY HIGH RISK   **3. HIGH RISK**

21

Fig 1.6: Risk grading in the brain's judgement area

The facility of the brain to make judgements, grade risks and anticipate how events are likely to unfold is essential to safe operational driving. It allows the driver to make effective plans and negotiate hazardous situations where high speed is involved.

Action Monitoring

When the proposed plan or manoeuvre has been thoroughly checked and cross-checked it is finally put into action. One final information process takes place during the time that the driving actions are actually being carried out. As shown in Figure 1.7 the driver forms

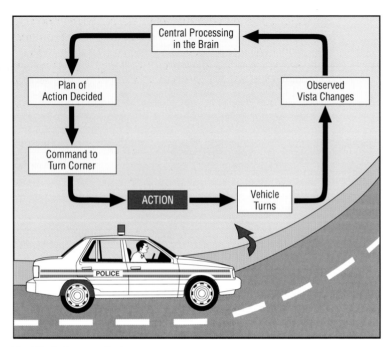

Fig 1.7: Action monitoring

an essential part of a closed loop man/machine system where he plays a vital role since he makes the decisions and judgements. The advanced driver develops the facility to monitor his driving actions as they are actually happening. Information is fed back into the processing system of the brain so that it can be continuously checked out for accuracy, appropriateness and safety. This facility to monitor and, if necessary modify driving actions, is an advanced skill that is acquired by the Police Driver after considerable experience and practice and it is one of the processes vital to the efficiency and safety of operational driving. It demands constant vigilance and intense concentration on the part of the driver and he must be alert to any change in circumstances and respond with alacrity to whatever new conditions are presented to him.

To summarise therefore Operational Police Driving depends on the Traffic Patrol Officer building up a vast selection of "motor programmes" that will meet every possible type of driving manoeuvre. It also requires development of the higher mental processes that provide him with situational awareness and the information to make accurate plans and form sound judgements. On the accuracy of his observations and the application of these skills may depend the outcome and safety of the operation and it is essential that every Police Advanced Driver fully understands the importance of these facilities. He must continue to build them up and develop them with constant training, experience and endless practice until he can perform them to the highest standards of proficiency.

23

Chapter 2
Limitations to Brain Processing

Introduction

It has been shown in the previous Chapter that Police Driving requires a level of skill, knowledge and experience well in advance of that required by the general motoring public. Tasks must be carried out with accuracy and proficiency, often at speed and under conditions not usually encountered by other drivers. In addition, the driver must use his vehicle handling skills to carry out Tactical Operations and other Police activities. All these require a very high level of mental processing powers and under certain circumstances operations may be so demanding that they stretch the processing powers of the brain to limits and even beyond.

Accurate and safe performance of the task ultimately depends on the available processing capacity of the brain. When demands are high and reserve capacity is reduced, the accuracy of decisions and the soundness of judgements may be impaired. In the more demanding phases of Police driving these impairments can not only reduce performance but can seriously compromise safety. It is important therefore to be aware that the brain has built-in limitations to processing which may reduce the effectiveness of the driving task in this way. These will be considered under the following headings:—

▶ Speed of Response

▶ Errors of Perception

▶ Limited Channel Capacity

▶ Limited Attention Span

▶ Memory Storage Capacity

Speed of Response

Once the Driver has made a decision and formed a plan it is necessary for some action to take place. Man however, is not an instant responder and one of the limitations to mental activities which affects driving is the time it takes to gather, process and eventually act upon incoming information. Sometimes the delay may be only a fraction of a second but on other occasions it may be much longer and, in rare circumstances, there may be no time to respond at all.

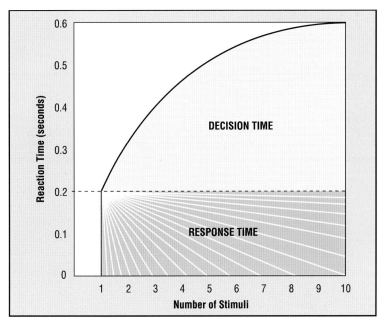

Fig 2.1: Reaction time composed of response and decision times

The time interval between the occurrence of a stimulus and completion of the appropriate response is called *the reaction time*. From Figure 2.I it can be seen that it is made up of two components— the time needed to decide on the action *(the decision time)* and the time to make the physical response itself *(the response time)*. In most people the response time is fairly constant but there is great variability in the time that a Driver needs to decide on what appropriate action to take. In a simple action, where perhaps only one decision is required, the overall time to react may be the same as the response time but as the task becomes more complex, or alternative choices exist, more time is needed for decisions, and the total reaction time is correspondingly longer.

At certain times during difficult Police Driving operations, the overall time to react may be increased if many complex decisions and judgements are required. Also, if there is pressure on the Driver to make a response quickly, the limited capacity for brain processing may result in it being made incorrectly and without due consideration of possible hazards and risks. Any delay in reaction could have catastrophic consequences during a high speed drive and Police Drivers must be aware of this danger and rely on the System of Car Control. This provides a structured way of dealing with every eventuality.

Errors of Perception

Under conditions of high speed driving yet another limitation to brain processing can lead to inaccuracies and danger. This is the problem of errors which can arise during the process of observation and visual scanning which the driver uses to build up a "perception model" of his surroundings. We know that the more accurate the model the more accurate the decisions and better the judgements that can be made. The Driver must be aware however, of some of the errors in perception which can occur during high speed operations when brain processing capacity is pushed to limits. These are:—

▶ *Illusions*—An error of perception can arise from "Illusion" which, if strong enough, can lead to wrong conclusions and incorrect assumptions or responses. To illustrate the problem of illusion the Reader should glance quickly at the message contained in the triangle in Figure 2.2 (a). After a first glance, he should go back and read the wording carefully to see whether his first reading of the message was correct or not. An example of a similar illusion is illustrated in Figure 2.2 (b). The Reader should estimate which of the lines he considers to be the longer and when he has decided, go back and check the accuracy of his estimation by actually measuring the length of each line with a ruler. This simple test illustrates some of the dangers which can result from illusion and errors of perception which can sometimes arise in driving. It is important to note that they become exaggerated when the drive is more demanding, and any wrong information conveyed to the brain can seriously compromise the safety of a high speed driving operation.

▶ *Habit and Expectancy*—Another error of perception is known as "driver habit". This can arise in a driver who has patrolled the same stretch of road on many occasions and has built up a familiar

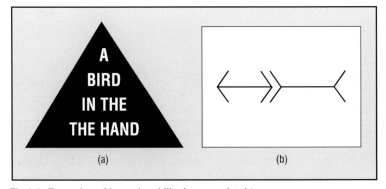

(a)   (b)

Fig 2.2: Examples of how visual illusions can lead to errors

"Perception Model" of the surroundings. He now associates the image, perhaps of a blind bend, with a situation where, on every previous occasion, no obstacle or hazard has been encountered. If circumstances change, however, and a hazard does exist round that corner, there may be a resulting mis-match between what the Driver expects to see and what, in fact, is the actual situation. This expectancy error and its effects may be a causative factor in serious road traffic accidents, and the Police Driver must be aware of the potential dangers which it can impose.

▶ *Regression Effects*—A further problem can arise as the result of the requirement by Police Drivers to use a variety of models of Patrol Vehicle all of which may have different handling characteristics and layout of controls. When an operation becomes difficult and rapid actions and fast responses are needed, there is a danger that the unwary Driver may confuse his control positions and revert to the handling techniques of the vehicle in which he trained, or with which he is perhaps more familiar. Many Drivers will have met the situation where they have reached for a control switch which is not in fact present in the vehicle which is being driven. Similar problems can occur with change from a manual to an automatic vehicle and "regression effects" can lead to driving which is inappropriate to some phases of Police Operations.

27

Limited Channel Capacity

There is evidence to suggest that the number of available connecting channels between different processing areas in the brain may be restricted. This means that in certain situations where information loading is high and processing is in demand, there may be a limit to the amount of data which the brain can actually handle. It is known that when one piece of information has entered the system, connecting channels tend to remain closed for further transmission until that piece of information has been fully processed. This is an important limitation which can affect performance during some aspects of Police Driving and may result in rationing or filtering of incoming information. Acquisition of incomplete data may ultimately affect decision and judgement making and the brain's limited channel capacity may impair the efficiency and safety of a high speed drive.

Limited Attention Span

Research has shown that many different stimuli can gain a Driver's attention. These can be auditory, like a radio call from the Control Room, or a warning horn from conflicting traffic; they may be from visual stimuli obtained by scanning the road ahead or noticing a warning light on the vehicle's instrument panel. The stimulus can even take the form of a thought which drives the brain to concentrate on some particular aspect of the task. People however, are limited in the attention which they can give to multiple stimuli, particularly when they arrive at the same time. We know from our own experience that it is difficult to listen attentively to two people talking at the same time, and Police Drivers are aware of the difficulties they sometimes have in concentrating where there is a multitude of radio instructions and other stimuli during a complex operation.

28

If an emergency arises during a situation like this, the driver may take longer to react and consequently the vehicle stopping distance will be increased.

During Advanced Training drivers learn to counteract this limitation by developing the facility to select and filter incoming stimuli so that they avoid the distracting ones but remain alert to the important ones which signal changing priorities. The experienced Driver adopts his own attention scanning drill and if necessary will re-establish attention by carrying out a "commentary" during a demanding drive.

Memory Storage Capacity

A further limitation to information processing arises from the restricted ability of the brain to hold information in its memory banks. During a drive all information flowing in from the senses is retained within what is known as the "Sensory Register". Images of the road ahead or sounds of traffic are retained for about two seconds while the brain decides whether to keep or reject them. Most are discarded to make room for the continuing flood of incoming new information but those that the brain chooses to retain are diverted into **short-term memory**. This is similar to a buffer store in a computer, and information is held there for only a limited time for use in decision making and judgement forming processes. Another difficulty arises from the limited capacity of short-term memory to hold more than about seven separate items. If new pieces of information come into the brain, the oldest entries are erased to make room for them even before they have time to be processed.

These two limitations represent potential problems to Police operations where it is sometimes necessary to hold several important items of information for a longer period. To counteract this limitation Police Drivers often develop their own techniques to hold on to information using a form of "Rehearsal". By this method, blocks of information are repeated in the mind and reinforced before they fade completely. This technique can be used to hold several vehicle registration numbers, telephone numbers or other complex data until they can be used or acted upon. The Driver should always be aware of the fact that even using techniques like these, short-term memory capacity is still limited and when the brain becomes saturated with information some may be lost. This may ultimately interfere with efficiency of performance of the operational task.

By contrast, the **long-term memory** store in the brain is vast and almost every piece of information or image which we have experienced during our lifetime is thought to be stored somewhere within its enormous memory banks. It too has limitations, although these are not ones of storage capacity but of recall of the information when it is required. Everyone has experienced difficulty in recalling names or numbers and bringing to conscious level some of the facts which have been previously learned. It must be appreciated therefore that recall difficulties can impose further restrictions to the driver's mental processing activities and at times of high demand may further reduce efficiency of task performance.

29

General Advice

In summary therefore, it is important for Police Drivers to appreciate that the brain has built-in limitations in its capacity to process information. Where operations involve carrying out several tasks simultaneously, there may be restriction of information processing channels available. When capacity is exceeded, decisions and judgements may be slower and less accurate and driving performance impaired. To counteract these limitations and assist the brain to process information the Driver can adopt the following procedures:—

► Maintain regular practice of driving techniques and learned manoeuvres to ensure that they are executed accurately and efficiently.

► Ensure that the brain is provided with as much information as possible about the surroundings by sharpening up observation and perceptual skills and by developing a keen sense of situational awareness.

► Make use of the advantages of the System of Car Control and keep the scan of attention as wide as possible so that it covers all aspects of the task and enables you to negotiate hazards.

Chapter 3
Operational Driving Stress

Introduction

Those who drive extensively are known to be vulnerable to the effects of driving stress. There is now evidence that repeated exposure to stress can not only make a Driver more accident-prone but, if added to the stresses of everyday life and work, can lead to stress related illness. The nature of Police Driving Operations makes exposure to some degree of operational stress an occupational hazard. Responding to a call-out, engaging in a fast pursuit or coping with difficult or hazardous incidents can bring about body responses which come under the general description of Stress Reactions. It is known that these can affect driving performance and must be fully understood by every Police Driver.

There have been many attempts to define stress, but the most useful definition in the present context is that it is *"the perception by the Driver of the demands placed on him and his ability to cope with these demands."* The important word in this definition is *perception* because each individual attaches his own meaning to a demand and interprets his own ability to cope with it. An operational situation perceived by one Driver as demanding and stressful may be viewed quite differently by another.

Responses to Stress

The responses to stressful situations are variable and often quite individual. Although still imperfectly understood, many years of investigation have led to volumes of published work on stress and its effects on the body. Those who wish to study stress in greater detail are referred to the many excellent works on the subject. The information presented in this Chapter is essentially practical and based mainly on the analysis of on-board vehicle studies carried out during Police and other Emergency Services operations. These have identified the following categories of operational stress to which Emergency Service Drivers may be exposed:—

▶ Anticipatory Responses

▶ Alarm Reaction

▶ Task Related Stress

► Life-threatening Stress
► Cumulative Incident Stress
► "Post-error" Dwell Reaction
► Work Related Stress

In a demanding or difficult drive, where brain processing is already stretched to limits, operational stressors may overload the system and further impair decision and judgement making and this may threaten the safety of the operation.

31

Anticipatory Responses

Many Police Officers are completely unaffected by the anticipation of facing difficult or demanding tasks. A few may experience slight apprehension before a particular shift or a special operation, but for a small minority, anticipatory stress can be a more regular and distressing occurrence. Those in this latter group often dread reporting for duty and have difficulty facing planned or unplanned events of the day. For them anticipatory stress responses are disruptive to their life and work.

For the majority of Police Drivers however, anticipatory stress reactions are quite normal and usually mild. Responses are typified by the commonly experienced "pre-examination nerves" and many of the related symptoms will be familiar to Police Officers about to face a final test drive during their Advanced Driver Training Course.

Anticipatory stress symptoms are often present on the evening before the event but they may start several days prior to it if normal healthy anticipation gives way to thoughts of dread. Sufferers may experience loss of appetite, difficulties in sleeping, or the inability to relax and switch-off an overactive mind. Some experience mild gastric irritation, nausea and occasionally, active vomiting. Others may have a frequent desire to pass urine or have slight looseness of the bowels up to the time of the anticipated event. Fortunately, these symptoms usually subside quite dramatically once the event is started and the mind becomes fully occupied with the business of the moment. Occasionally, however, symptoms fail to subside completely and in a few individuals they may be carried forward into the driving operation. It is here that when added to other operational stressors, they can cumulatively affect performance.

Alarm Reaction

This is the familiar response to the sudden startle caused by the sound of an alarm bell, an emergency telephone or the call-out by radio to attend an incident or engage in a fast pursuit. Reactions are similar to those experienced by an athlete on the starting line, a racing driver on the starting grid and indeed, anyone who is about to participate in an event which demands full concentration and maximum effort.

Symptoms include dryness of the mouth, sweating of the palms, pounding heart and a noticeable increase in rate and depth of breathing. They are brought about by the body's sympathetic nervous system and are vestiges of the basic life preserving "fight or flight" response found in more primitive members of the animal kingdom. It is this reflex and natural response to a demanding situation which prepares the animal to take flight or remain and oppose a predator. Hormonal and other chemical changes gear the animal up to providing its best performance.

In man, the same type of responses have the advantage that they raise the arousal state preparing him to give of his best in a stressful situation. The concept of "arousal" is shown in Figure 3.1 where the relationship between performance and the state of arousal takes the form of an inverted "U". It can be seen that with increasing arousal

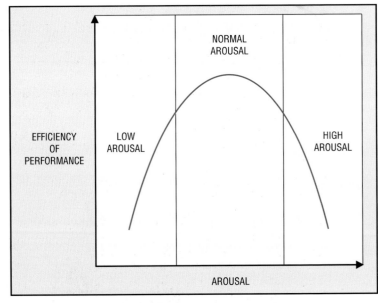

Fig 3.1: The concept of 'arousal'

the performance of a skilled task improves rapidly until it reaches an optimum level after which the beneficial effects fall away rapidly. In Police Driving Operations demands and stressors that reach beyond the optimum level negate the initial advantages of the high state of arousal and replace them with the more damaging effects of task related stress.

Task Related Stress

Most of the initial anticipatory stress responses usually subside by the time the Police Driver is fully engaged in an operation. If it goes well and according to plan, and is brought to a swift and satisfactory conclusion, stress reactions may be minimal and the crew may be entirely unaffected. If however, the drive becomes more difficult than usual the crew may encounter other stress factors which are known to affect the accuracy of performance. On-board studies have identified some of the factors which can cause stress (stressors) that can arise during more demanding Police Operations. They include the following:—

▶ Difficult traffic conditions which present the Driver with obstacles and hazards that impede his progress to the locus.

▶ Poor visibility or bad weather conditions which increase the difficulty and demands of the drive.

▶ Problems in locating or accessing the locus of an incident with consequent time delay.

▶ Lack of sufficient detail about conditions at the locus to enable plans to be made en-route to the scene.

▶ Pressure to reach the locus in as short a time as possible either to prevent escalation of an accident or to assist victims of injury.

▶ Anxieties about the possible need to carry out duties or activities such as resuscitation or first-aid measures which are less familiar to the Officer.

▶ Over-loading with multiple input of sensory information requiring brain processing that stretches capacity to limits.

Symptoms of stress build up as the operation progresses and become increasingly difficult to control. They are individual and variable but are usually an exaggeration of those experienced in the earlier stages of the drive. They may include profuse sweating of the palms of the hands, an increase in heart rate and blood pressure and changes in breathing which becomes faster and deeper. There is often tensing of muscle groups in the back and the neck and this may induce headache and back pain as the drive progresses. Occasionally mild tremor of muscle groups occurs and if it becomes excessive some control movements may be more difficult to perform.

Behavioural effects include difficulty in concentrating, forgetting short-time events such as details of a radio message. Overloading of brain processing may lead to the following:—

▶ *Omission*—where the Driver fails to respond to a situation or stimulus.

▶ *Error*—where the Driver does respond to a stimulus but takes an action which is inappropriate or dangerous.

▶ *Approximation*—where the Driver, faced with several tasks, may delay decision making until his workload falls to an acceptable level. He may consciously or subconsciously approximate and act on unsafe decisions and plans.

▶ *Coning of attention*—where the Driver reduces the span of his attention, distribution, concentrates on one narrow aspect of the task and misses potentially serious hazards.

Life-threatening Stress

During a fast response or a rapid pursuit the Police Driver may encounter situations which threaten the well-being and safety either of himself or the other occupants of his vehicle. In addition, a fast drive through busy streets or residential areas may pose a threat to members of the general public and other road users. In both instances this can lead to symptoms of life-threatening stress.

Experience of people involved in major incidents, serious accidents and disasters show that when they are caught up in a life-threatening situation they exhibit unusual behaviour and stress responses. In severe cases the brain attempts progressively to close down all information processing channels except those which it considers necessary to sustain life. There are two possible outcomes to this response. In the first the victim goes into a state of rigid muscle tension and "freezes" on the spot unable to respond to the pleas of onlookers or rescuers to take escape or evasive action. This extreme response has been encountered in aircraft and other serious fires where victims have tragically perished in what would normally be considered a survivable situation.

A second response to this type of severe stressor is sometimes described as "blind panic". In this situation motor programmes associated with escape sequences go into automatic operation. There is little or no monitoring or adjustment of the resulting motor actions and decision making, risk assessment and judgement taking are all completely abandoned. The affected person runs around in an unco-ordinated and uncontrolled manner, often entering danger zones instead of avoiding them.

Although it is recognised that these are particularly extreme reactions to very stressful situations it should be borne in mind by Police Drivers that even milder forms of life-threatening stress can potentially interfere with the speed and accuracy of decision making. They can also cause abandonment of the processes which co-ordinate driving manoeuvres and monitor their appropriateness and safety. Comparatively mild forms of this type of stress are now known to occur in Operational driving and the Officer faced with this type of situation should focus his concentration on his immediate driving task and not on the possible outcome of the operation.

35

Cumulative Incident Stress

By the nature of their duties, Police Drivers will be exposed sometime during their working life to the stress of very traumatic or distressing events. The psychological reactions to major incidents of this type

Fig 3.2: Circumstances that can lead to Cumulative Incident Stress

are examined in the next Chapter, but it should be borne in mind that repeated exposure to less distressing events can result in a build-up of stress responses which can eventually impair driving.

Police Officers may be required to attend road traffic accidents or other incidents several times within a single patrol. Although these may be distressing at the time, most Officers recover quickly with no residual deleterious effects on their work. Occasionally however, where such attendances have been frequent, particularly horrifying or have involved a friend, colleague or child the Officer may experience cumulative stress reactions (Figure 3.2).

In this state unpleasant or distressing images of a previous accident or incident may be recalled during a driving operation on some future occasion. It typically occurs where the surroundings and circumstances are similar to and evoke memories of, the previously distressing or traumatic event. The lingering memory "image" may be preferentially recalled from the memory store into the working memory area of the brain where the trace can cycle for a variable period of time. This recurrent cycling image interferes with normal interpretation and comparative processing activities essential to the accurate performance of the driving task. The blocking effect alters the accuracy of decision making and affects the soundness of judgements.

Post-error Dwell Reaction

Another mild stress reaction can result where an error of judgement is made or an inappropriate action is carried out inadvertently during a demanding operational drive. To the Police Driver such an error is uncharacteristic and may be perceived by him as displaying a lack of professionalism. A situation like this can result in post-error dwell effects which are similar to those experienced in cumulative incident stress. When it occurs, an image of the circumstances surrounding the error continues to cycle within the working memory area of the brain, blocking normal interpretative mental processing activities as it does so.

It can arise during a Final Test Drive when the Officer makes a minor error of judgement when under considerable strain to drive particularly accurately and well. Where "dwell reaction" follows the error, subsequent driving performance is often noted to be adversely affected as the driver becomes more pre-occupied with his mistake than with his current driving actions. The advice to drivers who find themselves in this situation either during training or under operations is to put all thoughts of the event to the back of the mind and concentrate firmly on the task ahead. By doing so, working memory is made available for the essential task of information processing.

Work Related Stress

Recent studies have indicated that driving may be affected by stressors other than those which arise during the operation itself. There is now evidence that some of the psycho-social hazards of Police work, including career, home and work problems may all have an important bearing on the nature and magnitude of operational stress reactions. Work stressors which are known to interact with operational driving are as follows:—

▶ Items of Police work which seem to lack variety or are perceived by the Officer as meaningless or an under-use of his skills.

▶ Career development or stagnation problems with uncertainties over promotion or job security.

▶ Work schedules that give rise to unpopular, unpredictable or unsocial working conditions.

▶ Deteriorating working relationships with senior officers and colleagues.

▶ Problems where conflicts exist between the demands of work and home life.

The tell-tale emotional and behavioural signs which accompany chronic work related stress problems often include:—

▶ Feelings of impatience or uneasiness if not constantly active.

▶ Difficulty in getting over to sleep because of lying awake thinking about the following day.

▶ A feeling that the mind cannot be fully cleared and that life is constantly full of crises.

▶ Progressive difficulty in making decisions about matters which would previously have caused no problems.

▶ Increased feelings of frustration, boredom, apathy and occasionally emotional withdrawal.

▶ Feelings of irritability with frequent rows and aggressive confrontations.

▶ Awareness that tasks are becoming more difficult and previous levels of working performance less easy to achieve.

▶ Physical symptoms of indigestion, nausea, frequent headaches, sweating and trembling.

37

Combating the Effects of Stress

It is important that the emotional and physical symptoms of stress are recognised by the Police Driver at an early stage so that they can be dealt with before they interact with driving skills. The first stage in combating stress is to develop an awareness of the many stressors which can be encountered during driving operations and the potential dangers and damaging effects which they can have on driving. The second line of defence is to rely on Training which provides protection against the stress effects on mental processing. The amount and quality of training and the consequent efficiency achieved by the Driver enables him to develop spare mental capacity and this allows him time to solve many of the problems causing stress. By creating time for planning his actions and tactics, he is better able to complete the task efficiently and well. The third important defence against continuing stress is maintenance of good standards of health with particular attention to diet, exercise and life-style.

These and other measures can be summarised in the following steps which assist in preventing stress impairment of driving performance. They are as follows:—

► Use all available mental processing capacity during stressful and demanding situations by putting training to good advantage. Well learned and practiced tasks are less likely to break down under stressful conditions.

► Maintain a high level of general health, take regular exercise and learn to relax whenever the opportunity presents - they are excellent defences against life and work stressors.

► Approach operational driving in a calm, confident manner knowing that you have the advanced skills which allow you to meet even the most demanding and stressful situation.

► Try if possible, to share difficult decision making with a colleague and work as part of a team.

► Remember that stress can be cumulative and keep domestic, social, work, career and other problems separate from those which can occur in driving operations.

► Don't allow previous stressful experiences to intrude into current operations. Concentrate on matters of the moment and not on the possible outcome of the operation.

► If you make a minor error or a misjudgement, avoid dwelling on it. Don't let it block working memory that is urgently needed for essential brain processing.

▶ Learn to recognise when you are becoming stressed and adjust your tasks and driving accordingly.

Chapter 4
Major Incident Stress

Introduction

One particular type of acute stress reaction may temporarily impair driving performance and if uncontrolled, adversely affect other police tasks. This is the stress which follows involvement by the Officer in a major incident or disaster. The United Kingdom has had its share of disasters and Traffic Patrol Officers have been involved in major fires, air crashes, road and rail accidents, "shootings" and terrorist incidents. From a practical viewpoint, involvement by Traffic Police Officers in major incidents includes the following:—

▶ Being caught up in a severely traumatic event like hostage taking or a shooting incident where the Officer's own life and well-being is threatened at the time. This type of personal involvement can lead to the condition of Post Traumatic Stress Disorder (PTSD).

▶ The Officer, although not personally threatened by the incident, may arrive early on the scene to be confronted by horrific sights which can deeply affect him. This can lead later to the condition of Post Incident Stress Reaction (PISR).

▶ Although not present at the locus of the incident, the Traffic Police Officer is involved on the fringe and may have to deal with bereaved or distressed relatives. This involvement, albeit indirect, may affect the Officer and can lead to a modified form of the Post Incident Stress Reaction.

No matter what type of involvement, the Officer can expect to experience some of a complex range of reactions which may affect not only his work but also his home life and personal relationships. For those who must return to duties that involve highly skilled activities like Operational Driving, there may be temporary impairment to task performance. It is important, therefore, to have an understanding of the various human reactions to a major incident and know the steps needed to gain full recovery from its aftermath.

Post Traumatic Stress Disorder (PTSD)

Fortunately, only a very small number of Traffic Police Officers become personally involved in a major incident and the severe psychological stressors which it entails. Experience of previous disasters has indicated that, if severe enough, those exposed to trauma of this kind may subsequently suffer the effects of PTSD. Studies have shown that of those who survive an incident and its horrific experience, many are unable to return to employment at the same level or to duties which they previously carried out.

Although there is still little known about PTSD, there is a number of practical features which distinguish it from the lesser traumas that can occur. The sheer severity of post-experience reaction is a major distinguishing feature but all affected persons show some degree of emotional numbing, increased arousal and hyper-vigilance and may be troubled by frequent and distressing "flash-backs". These intrusive thoughts and nightmares continually force the victim to relive his experience and often persist for several months or even years after the incident. While they are present they can impair work and home life and it may take skilled psychological handling to resolve the distress which the condition can bring.

41

Post Incident Stress Reaction (PISR)

This condition is usually confined to those who, although not personally involved in a life-threatening incident, have nonetheless been confronted by horrific or distressing sights when they have attended the scene. Although the condition shares many of the features of PTSD it is usually much less severe and of shorter duration. If handled promptly and professionally, the condition is unlikely to become chronic or subsequently interfere with the Officer's work and home life.

Practical experience with Rescue Services personnel who have been involved in major incidents shows that there are three well-defined phases during which certain reactions and responses may be expected. These are the Active, Reactive and Recovery phases:—

▶ *Active Phase*—An Emergency Service crew may be suddenly and unexpectedly confronted by overwhelming distressing sights and sounds at the scene of a major incident (Figure 4.1). The first reaction is often one of "mental paralysis" where the Officer does not know what actions he should take or where he should begin. This may be accompanied by physical symptoms such as nausea, actual vomiting or severe trembling. These symptoms last only briefly and are usually suppressed by the urgency of the situation and the need to get on with the work in hand. The busy rescuer is rarely totally incapacitated by even the most stress-inducing horrors but there is a danger that he may ignore his usual

Fig 4.1: Distressing scenes can lead to Post Incident Stress Reaction

judgement processes in the heat of the moment. The Police Officer must be aware of this and must not attempt a rescue until he is certain that he is neither endangering his own or other people's lives. A moment taken to sort out priorities, make decisions and formulate plans can improve the chances of a successful life saving rescue and reduce risks to health and wellbeing of the Officer himself. This is where disaster planning and rehearsal are of such importance.

▶ *Reactive Phase*—This stage in Post Incident Stress Reaction occurs usually when the Officer has completed his work at the locus and has returned to base. The next 24 to 48 hours may be devoted to making up sleep deficit and it is at this point that some of the more severe reactions can set in. They often take the form of intrusive thoughts or "flash-backs" to the event, mild panic attacks accompanied by nausea, loss of appetite and libido. Mood swings may occur and there may be episodes of tearfulness followed by mild depression. Sleep disturbance is an almost universal consequence which can add to problems during this phase. Other feelings and emotions include:—

▷ Mental numbness—where for some time after the incident the Officer may feel that events were unreal or like a bad dream.

▷ Helplessness—often accompanied by feelings of powerlessness and guilt at the lack of control over what has happened.

▷ Regret—for things which were or were not done and which the Officer believes might have resulted in a different outcome.

▷ Anger— with resentment at the senselessness of the accident or incident and needless injury or loss of life.

▷ Fear—of breaking-down, losing control or displaying what could be perceived by others as unprofessional or "unmanly" behaviour.

The extent of these physical symptoms, emotions and feelings vary with the nature of the incident. Where it involves victims such as families or children very strong feelings may be engendered. Other less common reactions can also follow and these include forgetfulness, unusual fatigue and physical symptoms like headaches, backpain, nausea, dizziness, tight chest and breathing difficulties.

43

▶ *Recovery Phase*—After a variable period the Rescuer moves into the Recovery Phase. This too takes a variable time to complete and an Officer left with more persistent symptoms may not be able to apply full concentration to his working tasks. In Operational Police Driving such impairment may lead, not only to loss of efficiency, but could possibly compromise the safety of an operation. It is imperative therefore that the Officer recognises any delay in his normal and expected recovery and seeks assistance if necessary before returning to the full range of driving duties. The persistent symptoms to watch out for are as follows:—

▷ Circumstances of the incident which remain in the forefront of the mind long after they have occurred.

▷ Persistence of mood swings, with feelings of tenseness, exhaustion, confusion and irritability.

▷ No reduction in the initial smouldering anger that was felt at the initial phase of the incident.

▷ Prolongation of disturbed sleep with frequent nightmares and occasional night "panic attacks".

▷ Change in interpersonal relationship with colleagues, friends and family.

▷ Withdrawal behaviour and a desire to avoid contact with colleagues who were similarly involved in the incident.

▷ Awareness that skilled tasks are being less well performed and that unusual difficulties are being experienced in coping with more complex actions and manoeuvres.

▷ A noticeable increase in smoking and drinking habits, often in the misguided attempt to calm the nerves and suppress unpleasant thoughts.

▷ Continuing reliance on medications, particularly those that have been prescribed to assist sleep or alter mood.

Professional Support

Each individual has his own way of coping with stress reactions in the aftermath of a major incident or disaster. Some obtain relief from the emotional support of others and find that talking about their feelings and reactions with other Officers who have had similar experience greatly assists them to cope with their own problems. Others find that it is better to be alone or with family and close friends until the recovery phase is complete.

Each Police Force throughout the United Kingdom has set up its own organisation and mechanism to deal with the stress reactions suffered by Officers in the event of a major disaster. Professional Support Teams are now very skilled in handling those people who have been exposed to Post Traumatic or Post Incident Stress Reactions and the Officer should not hesitate to avail himself of whatever professional assistance is offered. Careful monitoring of the progress and intervention if necessary at an early stage can help in the transition from one phase to another until recovery is complete. There are many different techniques used to support personnel after a major incident and it is not the purpose of this Book to discuss their various merits. Most of them however include the following features and experience has shown that they can greatly assist towards recovery:—

▶ A fully trained team on standby and available to answer whatever questions the Officer may pose about his reactions to the situation, and the subsequent effects it might have on his health.

▶ Discussing problems as part of a group where sharing of experiences can promote the use of the Officer's own strengths towards recovery.

▶ Rehearsal of the "incident story" in a controlled and monitored way that allows re-awakening of the emotions so that they can be tolerated and coped with.

▶ Use of psychological techniques which help to combat low mood, guilt at surviving, persistent arousal and repeated intrusive thoughts.

▶ Medical intervention to break the vicious cycle of sleeplessness, fatigue and mood swings.

Police Officers caught up in a major incident should make use of whatever professional support is on offer to ensure that recovery is both rapid and complete. They should bear in mind the possible temporary adverse effects on driving and other task performance and always seek medical advice before returning to full operational driving duties.

Chapter 5
Attitudes and Driving Behaviour

Introduction

Emotions and attitudes are aspects of human nature which anyone can exhibit at some time or another. They reflect on all our actions including those of driving and there is a danger in letting them overrule our ability to make sensible decisions and plan our actions. An attitude can be defined as *"the state of mind in which a person engages in a task,"* and for many years it has been known that negative attitudes can impair the performance of a skilled motor task. When the task is a complex one like driving, any decrement of performance can compromise safety and it is believed that a significant number of road traffic accidents result from a bad attitude or emotion arising in the driver.

Effects of Attitudes on Driving

Negative attitudes can influence driving at all stages in the learning process. During the early learning phase a driver usually displays positive attitudes towards his driving. His behaviour pattern is motivated by the desire to gain knowledge, learn driving techniques, pass his test and ultimately achieve the freedom and convenience of a motor vehicle. When they occur, accidents within this group are usually relatively minor and mostly due to inexperience.

After passing the test some inexperienced and usually younger drivers go on to display dangerous unwanted attitudes and behaviour patterns which carry the common descriptor of "hot driver" or "boy racer." Many within this group grossly overestimate their own abilities and tend to show off in front of their peers, or display behaviour that shows total disregard for the safety of themselves and others. No matter the age or experience, there is a recognised post-training danger period where the driver may be under pressure from his peer group to show off his newly acquired driving skills and may exceed his abilities when doing so.

Advancing years and more experience usually lead to safer habits and the development of more positive attitudes to driving. As knowledge and experience are gained, behaviour patterns also change. With career and family responsibilities they become more positive and attitudes of an immature, negative and dangerous kind are generally suppressed. There is a much lower incidence of serious road traffic accidents attributable to human behaviour amongst the more senior and experienced groups.

Until recently it had been believed that those trained to a high level of Advanced Driving Proficiency suppress negative attitudes and it was assumed that behaviour played little or no part in their driving. On board work-profile analyses however have revealed that, under demanding or fatiguing driving conditions like a Rapid Response or a Fast Pursuit, positive attitudes and emotions, can be replaced by more dangerous negative ones. These can develop quite insidiously and can progressively impair information processing in the brain and as a result, compromise the safety of the driving operation.

47

Some of the Attitudes and Emotions which can occur during demanding phases of police driving are summarised in Figure 5.1 and include the following:—

▶ *Stress Induced Negative Attitudes*
▶ *Fatigue Generated Emotions*

Recognition that negative attitudes, emotions and atypical behaviour can arise in even the most highly trained and experienced driver has led to the expansion of the training philosophy which has traditionally been based on knowledge, skill and experience. It now includes Attitude Training which has become accepted as a prominent component of many Police Advanced Driving Courses. This Chapter examines some of the issues relating to attitudes, emotions and patterns of behaviour which can intrude into the demanding police drive.

Stress Induced Negative Attitudes

In a previous Chapter it was shown that when a vehicle crew is called out to engage in a Rapid Response, there is initially some degree of alarm reaction. Studies show that, in this high state of arousal previously suppressed attitudes may be released and some of those which are in danger of emerging during this phase are as follows:—

▶ *Impatience*—in his keeness to get to the locus in the shortest time the driver may become impatient and forget the importance of maintaining a calm approach to the driving task.

▶ *Intolerance*—During this phase the stressed police driver may consider that he has priority over other road users and display

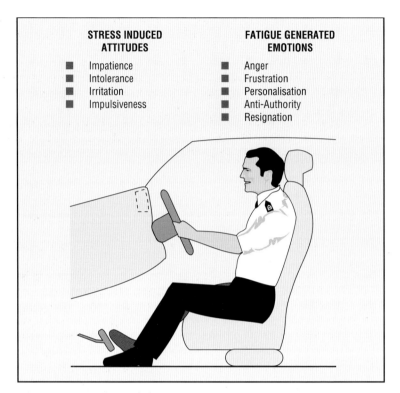

STRESS INDUCED ATTITUDES	FATIGUE GENERATED EMOTIONS
■ Impatience	■ Anger
■ Intolerance	■ Frustration
■ Irritation	■ Personalisation
■ Impulsiveness	■ Anti-Authority
	■ Resignation

Fig 5.1: Attitudes and emotions which must be avoided in a demanding drive

intolerance of those whose driving skills he considers inferior to his own.

▶ *Aggression*—Normally suppressed emotions like aggression and anger can be released in the driver when obstacles appear to thwart access to the locus.

▶ *Impulsiveness*—where time is short there is the temptation to make immediate decisions or take impulsive actions without analysing alternatives or assessing risks.

▶ *Machismo complex*—Under stress, a driver may revert to a behaviour pattern in which decisions and actions are ill-considered and inappropriate. In this frame of mind he believes that he possesses superior knowledge and skills and this can lead to risk-taking purely to impress others.

▶ *Justifying risk*—When under pressure, Emergency Service vehicle crews may forget the responsibilities which they have for the safety and well-being of other road users. Risks cannot be justified on the basis that they are in a "noble" cause and attitudes generated by an urgency to reach the locus quickly or to assist the injured cannot be excused.

There are many more attitudes and behaviour patterns which training and experience normally inhibit in the Police Driver but which are in danger of re-emerging during times of stress. The Reader may be able to identify others from his own experience and it is important that he does so, keeping an awareness that they can interfere with his operational driving tasks.

Fatigue Generated Emotions

49

On-board and other studies have revealed that when a police operation, like a fast pursuit, is difficult to bring to a conclusion or is not completely controlled, the crew may begin to lose the beneficial effects of the initial high arousal state. They go into what is known as the "Exhaustive Phase" where fatigue can set in and alertness decline. Under these circumstances the driver may release inhibition of the emotions which would normally be suppressed as part of his professional training. The major ones which can appear during an exhausting, difficult and demanding drive are as follows:—

► *Anger*—at the apparent failure to bring the pursuit to a satisfactory conclusion, or at the behaviour of the pursued driver.

► *Frustration*—at the difficulties in maintaining control of the operation or apparently being outwitted by an inexperienced and rank bad driver.

► *Personalisation*—where the crew get into personal conflict with the pursued driver and occasionally with others involved in the operation. Release of this powerful negative attitude is often betrayed in speech with remarks like "I-will-get-him-if-it-kills-me". The tragedy is that, if uncontrolled, this emotion can indeed be a killer if the driver becomes obsessively determined to achieve his objective no matter what the cost.

► *Anti-authority Feelings*—which stem from resentment by the crew at being told what they must or must not do. It can arise when a pursuit is suddenly called off for no apparent reason. Control Room staff may be the target of such anti-authority feelings when it is forgotten in the heat of the moment that they are probably in receipt of information perhaps not available to the crew.

► *Resignation*—which occurs when the pursuit is prolonged, the crew are fatigued and they feel that any action they take will make little or no difference to the outcome of the situation. In this state the driver tries to avoid making further decisions or accepting responsibility for the subsequent outcome.

These emotions and attitudes are all very powerful and can seriously impair brain processing at a time when capacity is already stretched to limits. Police crews must be aware of their vulnerability to negative attitudes and fully understand the destructive and dangerous consequences of allowing them to intrude into driving operations.

Effects of Attitudes on Brain Processing

In a previous Chapter it was shown that during a demanding or stressful drive brain processing may reach limits of capacity. Stress effects may further reduce the remaining available processing capacity and when they release previously suppressed emotions and attitudes can tip the balance and interfere with brain processing by:—

► Reducing channels that interconnect memory banks to the working memory area and the two main processing centres involved in decision and judgement making. The outcome is that plans of action are less accurate, decisions are slower and judgements impaired at a time when they are most required.

► Reducing observation scanning with a narrowing of the field of visual sensory input.

► Acquiring an incomplete and possibly inaccurate "picture" of the surroundings which may lead to actions and decisions that are likewise less accurate.

► Overloading the brain processing system causing a selective bypass of hazard assessment which results in the driver taking risky actions.

► Limiting attention distribution as a consequence of which driving operations are inadequately monitored and developing hazards and risk factors are not properly assessed.

Red Mist

Severe coning of attention can result when the driver becomes caught up emotionally in the pursuit. When negative attitudes and emotions take over, they can cause him to become obsessively determined to achieve some objective. This can be catching the pursued vehicle, arresting the villain or reaching the incident in record time. In this state, attention scan is very severely reduced and the driver is no longer capable of assessing risks or evaluating and judging his actions. He has now entered into a most dangerous situation, popularly known as "Red Mist". Here his attention is focussed into such a small area (usually the vehicle which is being pursued) that there is virtually no monitoring of other aspects of the pursuit. In parallel with this, visual scanning may also be reduced and the visual field restricted to a small zone. Hazards like traffic or adverse road conditions are neither detected nor evaluated properly.

Other Factors affecting Attitudes and Emotions

Pre-disposing Factors

There is some evidence to suggest that negative attitudes may begin to develop in the events which lead up to the driving task. They may arise in the home as a result of social/domestic, family, financial or other life problems. They can develop during the drive to work where, like other road users, the Officer may be exposed to the behaviour of less considerate motorists.

Prior to entering his patrol vehicle he can be exposed to stresses arising from other aspects of his work. Experience has suggested that the approach to non-driving duties may reflect on the Traffic Police Officer's attitudes and behaviour during demanding driving operations. Those who tend to approach their work with negative attitudes often consider that their tasks lack variety or are meaningless and that there is under-use of their abilities. They perceive their work as over-demanding or allowing only limited control over its content. Perceived lack of involvement in decision making can also add to the problem, as can poor relationships with colleagues and senior officers. Feelings of career stagnation and promotion uncertainties are all recognised as important pre-conditioners to driving attitude problems that can be carried over into operational driving tasks.

Influence of Personality

Although it is recognised that negative attitudes and emotions may arise when the driver is under stressful or fatiguing situations, there is some evidence that personality may also play a significant role. Personality is the term used to embrace all the behavioural characteristics associated with an individual, and at a simple level can be considered within two broad dimensions Stable/Unstable and Introverted/Extroverted. Some of the typical characteristic traits associated with the these dimensions are summarised in Figure 5.2. There are other much more detailed analyses of personality for a given individual but this basic model is useful in categorising those who, like police drivers, are required to perform complex tasks.

Most people will be around the average in both dimensions but as personality departs from the norm, the associated characteristics become more marked. Those who fall into quadrant (A) of Figure 5.2

are usually regarded by others as tending towards aggressive or impulsive behaviour, whilst those in quadrant (B) are considered outgoing and responsive by nature and usually show qualities of leadership and good motivation towards their work. Those with the tendency to stable but introverted characteristics, as in quadrant (C), are normally considered reliable, careful, thoughtful and self-controlled individuals who remain calm in a crisis. Those who identify with the characteristics of quadrant (D) tend to be moody, anxious and pessimistic with a more reserved attitude towards their colleagues. The reader should be able to locate his own personality type and be aware that this can influence the development of attitudes which he should guard against under demanding driving conditions.

As well as attempting to recognise his own personality traits it may be useful for the Officer to consider some of the characteristics which he may observe in others. The well known ones are:—

▶ **'The Fast Operator'**—who tends to do everything at the double when working normally. Under pressure his behaviour pattern is exaggerated and he can easily make silly mistakes when driving.

▶ **'The Strong Type'**—who never admits to having any weaknesses and despises them in others. In high demand driving operations this personality type usually fails to admit to limitations and often exceeds them with serious consequences.

▶ **'The Approval Seeker'**—who thrives on the praise of others and modifies his behaviour and actions to obtain this. He tends to show off and when driving conditions become difficult or demanding takes risks in order to achieve his aim.

▶ **'The Perfectionist'**—who, in normal duties and work always takes on too much and often fails to complete tasks satisfactorily. People like this fail to hand in reports on time because they feel they require to be 100% perfect—an ideal which is unattainable. Under pressure they are unable to prioritise tasks and may neglect some important aspect of their driving which compromises the safety of the operation.

There are many other personality traits which the reader may have come up against in others but if he can recognise his own personality type he may be able to control unwanted emotions and attitudes before they become dangerous.

Effects of Minor Illness

Minor medical conditions like the common cold, influenza or hay fever can all affect mood and generate negative attitudes towards driving. They can cause mood swings that make the driver feel

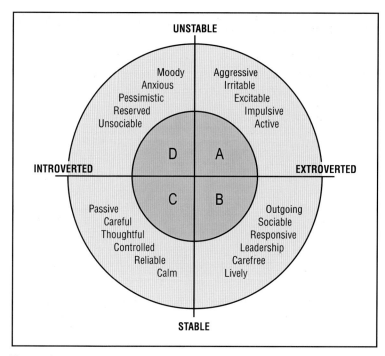

UNSTABLE

Moody	Aggressive
Anxious	Irritable
Pessimistic	Excitable
Reserved	Impulsive
Unsociable	Active

D   A

INTROVERTED   EXTROVERTED

53

C   B

Passive	Outgoing
Careful	Sociable
Thoughtful	Responsive
Controlled	Leadership
Reliable	Carefree
Calm	Lively

STABLE

Fig 5.2: A two-dimensional model of personality

anxious, irritable and less tolerant to minor inconveniences. Unpleasant symptoms can make him less alert and impair both his concentration and dimensional judgements. Measurements of driving performance by sufferers of minor conditions have shown that there are marked decrements in several aspects of the task which it is now believed can lead to road traffic accidents.

It is also important to remember that many "cold cures" and medicines can cause drowsiness and other side effects. The driver should therefore be careful and selective in their use and pay strict attention to the instructions given on the container. A further influence on attitudes is found in the minor depression which occasionally arises in the recovery phase of a viral illness including influenza, when there may be quite marked variations of mood. These can significantly impair task performance and, in more serious forms, can affect the safety of the drive.

Residual Blood Alcohol

Even the most self-disciplined driver who meticulously avoids drinking and driving may be unaware of the attitude changing effects of even very tiny amounts of residual blood alcohol. Although the effects of low levels of alcohol on driving are not fully understood, a number of studies would suggest that there may be some impairment of task performance even at surprisingly low values. The driver should be aware that effects on mood and behaviour can occur even in the absence of an overt hangover. Different drinks affect people in different ways and the time to reduce blood alcohol to safe levels is variable. The only real way of averting the danger is either to avoid alcohol consumption completely or allow plenty of time for *all* alcohol to be removed from the bloodstream. A rough guide is that, on average, it takes one hour for each unit of alcohol ingested (one measure of spirit = one unit) to be cleared from the bloodstream. It is important to remember that minute quantities can remain long after normal clearance time and may predispose the driver to negative attitude problems in demanding situations. Police drivers must restrict their social drinking in terms of quantity consumed and allow a sufficient time margin before going on duty to allow full blood clearance to occur.

Low Blood Sugar

It is known that throughout the working day blood sugar may drop to quite low levels at certain times. Some people react to these troughs by displaying mood changes like irritability, apathy and drowsiness. In themselves these symptoms can interfere with the driving task and the secondary attitudes which they create must be avoided if driving is to remain safe. If a driver finds that he is susceptible to episodes of low blood sugar, a simple remedy is to eat a boiled sweet or some other source of glucose that will help to restore blood sugar to more acceptable levels. Regular light meals also help to maintain levels, prevent troughs of low blood sugar and avoid associated mood changes.

Cyclical Mood Swings

Female drivers are aware of the hormonal changes which occur during the menstrual cycle and some drivers may experience mild mood swings prior to and during the time of the menstrual period. At its most extreme, some women suffer from the effects of pre-menstrual tension (PMT) during which judgemental skills and task performance may be affected to some degree. By contrast, at mid-cycle, the female driver has particularly high powers of concentration and driving abilities may actually improve at this time.

Few men however appreciate that they too may be prone to mood swings related to cyclical hormonal changes. The male driver is at some disadvantage however, in that unlike his female counterpart, he is usually unable to predict the time of their occurrence. All drivers should be aware that metabolic, chemical and hormonal changes occurring in both males and females may alter mood and result in attitudes that affect driving performance. It is important that the driver tries to recognise his or her own particular cyclical mood swings and during these times be aware of their consequences and make allowances for them in his driving.

Practical Advice

In order to reduce the adverse effects of negative attitudes, emotions and behaviour patterns the driver is urged to take the following practical steps:—

55

► Maintain a calm, considered, professional approach when driving in an emergency situation.

► Apply the techniques which have been learned during training and concentrate on performing all driving actions and manoeuvres with precision and accuracy.

► Maintain a wide range of attention scanning and prevent dangerous coning of attention into a "Red Mist" situation.

► Concentrate on matters of the moment rather than on the possible final outcome of the drive.

► Avoid behaviour and talk which "personalises" the pursuit or creates dangerous attitudes between you and the driver you are pursuing or others involved in the pursuit.

► Try to identify your own personality type and get to know its associated behaviour patterns. This may help to reduce the risk of unwanted attitudes and emotions occurring during a difficult driving operation.

► Be wary of minor medical conditions which can cause mood changes. If you require to treat a condition be certain that the medication you are taking does not produce side effects and if you are in any doubt, do not undertake driving operations until you have sought medical advice.

Chapter 6
Vision and Observation

Introduction

The driver uses several senses to gather information about himself, his vehicle and his surroundings. Of the five senses in the body, vision is the most commonly used and accounts for some 95% of the sensory input to the brain during police driving tasks. Vision is used to judge distances, gauge depths, search for clues about hazards on the road ahead as well as to interpret colour signals and read vehicle instruments. During their training, Police Drivers develop very high powers of observational skills and learn to make the fullest use of visual sensory input information. This becomes of significance during more demanding tasks and it is important that the driver has a knowledge of the workings of the human eye and understands the basic principles of vision.

Functional Anatomy of the Eye

In principle, the eye is like a camera (Figure 6.1). There is a *lens* system at the front to collect and focus light rays; the *iris* acts like a camera aperture control and the *retina* corresponds to the film which captures the images. There are even the equivalents of lens caps in the form of eyelids and for added safety, the eyes are cradled in housings deep inside bony sockets in the skull. A highly lubricated surface ensures continual smooth swivelling of the eye by six strip-like muscles which also act to anchor the eyeball securely in place.

The white outer layer of the eyeball has a transparent circular segment called the *cornea* that bulges at the front to let light into the eye. About 75% of incoming light is bent or refracted by the cornea and the light rays are directed towards the centre of the eye. Immediately behind the cornea there is a ring of coloured muscle, the iris, that surrounds the pupil and opens and closes the aperture to control the amount of light entering. In bright conditions the iris can narrow down to restrict light entry, while in the dark it can open to its maximum extent, gathering in whatever light there is available.

Fine image adjustment is provided by the lens which changes shape and provides a sharp image on the light sensitive surface of the retina.

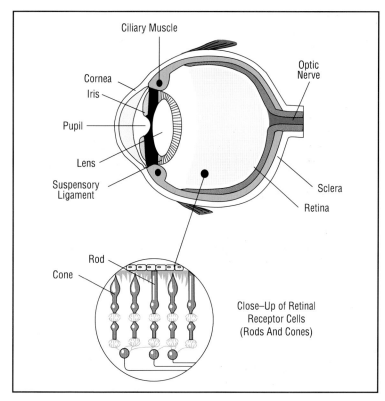

Fig 6.1: Functional anatomy of the eye

The lens is held in place by very fine *suspensory ligaments* which pull on and flatten it when the eye is at rest. In this state objects more than twenty feet away are brought into sharp focus. To focus on nearer objects the ciliary ligaments make the lens take up a more rounded shape.

Finally, the refracted light rays are focussed on to the retina—the film of the eye's camera. Here, light energy is converted into electrical nerve signals by photoreceptor cells which are served by multiple nerve connections. The electrical messages thus generated are sent up the *optic nerve* which connects with the brain itself. Within the visual cortex of the brain incoming signals are unscrambled and converted into mental images of the objects which have been viewed.

The light sensitive retina contains two types of cells which, because of their distinctive shapes, are known as rods and cones (Figure 6.1). The *cones* are densely distributed around the central area of the retina and are designed to detect very fine detail of viewed images. They need a lot of light to operate however, and work best in bright daylight. They are also used to differentiate colours. The other types of cells, known as **rods**, are very light sensitive and are distributed around the periphery of the retina. Collectively they create a coarse grey image which is nevertheless adequate for seeing in poorer light conditions, and useful for night driving. Rods, unlike cones, have no ability to detect different colours.

The distribution of rods and cones gives a combination of light sensitive cells that provide the driver with both day and night vision. In the middle of the retina, and in direct line from the pupil there is a small round area tightly packed with cones, *the fovea*. This creates an area of sharpest vision and to inspect something closely we focus its image directly onto this area (Figure 6.2).

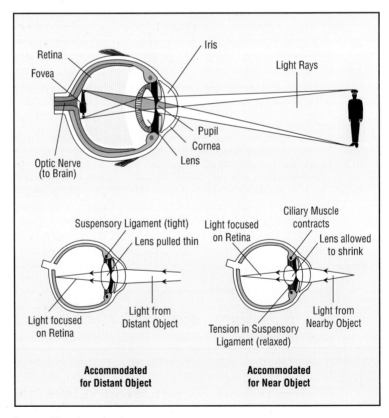

Fig 6.2: Visual mechanisms

Away from the central fovea, the proportion of cones declines until at the edges of the retina light cells are made up mostly of rods. This arrangement gives good peripheral vision of faint objects but no real detail. Although the driver can see something moving in the edges of the field of vision, he needs to look directly at the object and bring it to focus on the central fovea to see what it is in detail. Normally the eyes move about rapidly so that each part of the field of view falls on the central area in turn. This allows the brain to build up a sharp picture of the entire surroundings.

Visual Mechanisms

Accommodation

By the process of accommodation the eye is able to bring objects into sharp focus at distances ranging from infinity to the nearest point of distinct vision. Hold up a finger and you can focus sharply on it leaving the background blurred. Now bring the background into focus and the finger becomes indistinct. Focussing on the close finger was achieved by a change in the curvature of the lens brought about by the ciliary muscles. When the ciliary muscles are relaxed accommodation is in the resting position and the eyes are focused at infinity. When there is a requirement to view close objects, the ciliary muscles compress the lens and they are brought into focus (Figure 6.2).

The process of accommodation is of great importance in driving but it can be affected by several factors including age of the driver and level of prevailing light conditions. Age reduces the power and speed of accommodation as the lens gradually loses its elasticity and the nearpoint of sharp focus recedes. When the nearpoint has receded beyond twenty five centimetres the condition is called presbyopia (or long-sight of age) and corrective spectacles are needed to restore normal vision. The other factor critical to accommodation is the amount of light falling on the viewed object. When poor light falls on a distant object it requires to be closer to the eye to remain in focus. Contrast is another important factor and the more an object stands out against its background the better are the powers of accommodation.

Stereoscopic Vision and Distance Judgement

When the driver looks at an object, each eye forms its own image so that two sets of impulses are sent to the brain. The brain combines these impulses so that he sees only one object and not two. However,

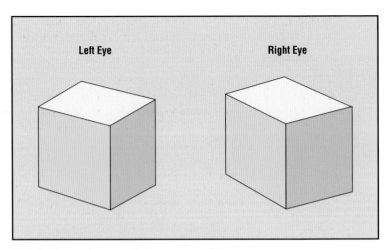

Fig 6.3: The mechanism of stereoscopic vision

because the eyes are spaced apart, they do not have exactly the same view of the object. It can be seen from Figure 6.3 that the left eye sees more of the left side of the object and the right eye sees more of the right side. When the brain combines the information from both eyes it gives the impression that the object is three-dimensional rather than flat.

The driver uses a number of different mechanisms to judge distances. If the object viewed is less than about 12 metres away, the eye muscles contract to rotate the eyeballs slightly inwards. Stretch receptors in the eye muscles send impulses to the brain making it aware of how much inward movement has been required and this allows the driver to gauge the distance that the object is away from him. For objects that are further away he judges distance by comparing the size of familiar objects or detecting the apparent movement of the viewed object against its background.

Adjusting to Brightness

The eye has two ways of adjusting to different levels of brightness. The first results from changing the diameter of the iris to alter the amount of light falling on the sensitive light cells of the retina. The other mechanism is through complex chemical changes which allow the retina to adapt to different light conditions. Coming from bright daylight into a dark room, causes dark adaptation by chemical changes which take place in the cones over a period of about seven minutes. Further chemical changes take another thirty minutes until full adaptation by the rods is achieved. When entering the dark room, the viewer can see very little at first, but when the chemical adaptation mechanism is complete objects gradually become visible. Thanks to this facility a driver can see equally well in moonlight and in the brightest sunlight even although the light levels may differ by a hundred thousand fold.

The opposite process of adaptation to bright light conditions is very much quicker than dark adaptation. Coming from the dark into a well lit room causes photochemical processes that reduce the sensitivity of the retina in a few tenths of a second allowing clear vision in the brightness.

Despite this flexibility it is possible for too much light to fall on the eye. In very bright sunshine or where sunlight is reflected from snow or water, the driver may be exposed to excessive light entering the eye. The iris closing mechanism attempts to reduce the amount falling on the retina and photo chemical adaptation alters the sensitivity of the retina to cope with very bright light. Under such driving conditions the wearing of appropriate sunglasses can help to maintain good vision and reduce eyestrain. Sunglasses should be of impact resistant type, have thin metal frames to minimise visual obstruction, and should be constructed from materials that give safety and strength. The lenses should have good refractive optical quality and should provide adequate light transmittance and appropriate filtration characteristics.

Colour Vision

Within the retina there are three types of colour sensitive cones. All respond to more than one colour but each is particularly sensitive to either blue, green or yellow light. Red light falling on the retina stimulates yellow sensitive cones more than the green sensitive ones and the difference is interpreted by the brain as redness. Other colours are detected by similar proportional colour sensitivity and when all three types are stimulated in the right proportions they give the appropriate colour sensation. About 8% of men and 0.5% of women are known to suffer from one or other form of colour blindness. Rarely is there total inability to distinguish colours from shades of grey and more often there is failure to discriminate between the colours red, brown or green. Most drivers who are colour blind are still able to distinguish traffic lights by their intensity and position without relying on true colour discrimination. Likewise green direction signs on trunk roads and blue direction signs on motorways present no problems to the colour defective driver since he relies on contrast for this interpretation. It is comforting to note that several studies have shown that there is no correlation between the occurrence of road traffic accidents and presence of colour defects in the driver.

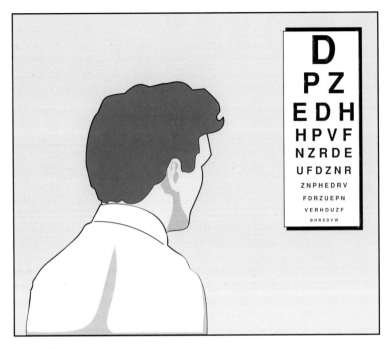

Fig 6.4: Testing visual acuity using an eye chart

Visual Acuity

This is the ability to see the finest details of objects and surfaces. It is linked to the resolving power of the eye's optical system and since the sensitive light receptors tire rapidly, the eyes must make continual small movements to preserve normal acuteness of vision. As previously stated, the central part of the retina contains cones only and in good light is the area of sharpest vision. It is in this area that we measure visual acuity by means of eye charts (Figure 6.4). Here we may have normal 6/6 vision, i.e. the ability to see at 6 metres that which a normal individual is capable of seeing at that range. With the condition of myopia a driver's vision may be reduced to 6/12 and this means that he requires to be at 6 metres to see what a person with normal vision can see at 12 metres. Many Police drivers have higher than normal visual acuity and can resolve to a level of 6/4, in that they can see at 6 metres that which the average person would have to be a 4 metres to see clearly. Common defects in visual acuity including long sightedness (hypermetropia), short sightedness (myopia), and astigmatism can all be corrected by spectacles, so that many drivers can meet vision standards even though their eyesight may not be perfect.

Assisting Visual Mechanisms

Visual mechanisms can be assisted in a number of ways so that the driver can make full use of his powers of observation and gather accurate information about himself, his vehicle and his surroundings. The ways in which vision can be assisted are as follows.

Improvement in Optical Visibility

To assist vision and allow it to work as efficiently as possible, the driver should aim to achieve the best possible view around the vehicle. He should ensure that the windscreen and the windows are clean inside and out and that the windscreen wipers and washers are in good working order. In poor weather conditions of fog, heavy rain, snow or fading daylight, visibility may be reduced. To assist visual mechanisms in those conditions the speed of driving should be reduced so that time is available to take avoiding action if needed. Headlight beams should be set to suit the conditions and visual clues like hazard warning lines and reflective studs, should all be used to assist visual mechanisms in poor driving conditions.

63

Visual Scanning

Good visual scanning techniques assist the brain to build up an accurate picture of the surroundings. The scanning movements of the eyes should sweep the whole environment from far distance, back through middle distance to foreground. The development of scanning movements of this type into a repetitious and regular habit ensures that no potential hazard is missed. It enables the driver to pinpoint areas of risk and should involve the use of mirrors and over-the-shoulder checks if appropriate. The driver can also use to his advantage the properties of the light sensitive rod cells distributed on the periphery of the retina. These are particularly useful in detecting movements and by using this mechanism he can be alerted to areas needing closer visual examination.

Adjusting Vehicle Speed

To anticipate events at high speed the driver requires efficient scanning techniques. He should be aware that the faster the speed the further ahead he requires to look to allow sufficient time to react. It is also important to note that as speed increases less foreground detail can be seen and in areas of high density traffic the driver should slow down to take in as much foreground information as possible. He should also be aware that visual muscles can fatigue during prolonged driving in poor visibility conditions and the vehicle's speed should be slowed under these circumstances.

Gaining Additional Visual Clues and Observation Links

The driver should use all available sources of visual information to assist his observational skills. When forward view from the vehicle is restricted alternative sources can assist brain information processing. Observation links like mobile shops, school buses, warn of the possible presence of children in the vicinity. Commercial vehicles are likely to halt at associated premises and petrol stations, public houses and other buildings signal the possibility of vehicle movements in and out of parking places. Likewise, mud and animal deposits on the road create a link with slow moving agricultural vehicles or herds of animals round an approaching bend. Other visual clues about approaching traffic and road layout can be obtained from reflections in shop windows, the curvature in a line of lamp standards or trees and breaks in hedges, walls and fences. All these factors give the driver additional information which assists his visual mechanisms to build up a more accurate and complete picture of the surroundings.

Adjusting to Night Driving

Under conditions of low light the ability to see the road ahead declines as edges become less distinct and contrasts and colours fade. It is especially important under these driving conditions to improve optical transmission through windows and windscreens by keeping them clean and regularly washed and wiped. Windscreen grease and dirt tend to break up the viewed light source and increase the hazard of glare. Attention to these simple precautions can greatly assist the visual mechanism in improving safety and comfort of night driving.

The appropriate headlight beam setting to suit prevailing conditions helps to improve observation and assist vision. Other useful information about the road ahead can be obtained from the lights of other vehicles, hazard warning posts and reflective studs. Assistance can be given to vision under night driving conditions by reducing speed when leaving a brightly lit area in order to allow retinal adaptation to take place.

Finally, it should be remembered that although visual perception and good observations are important to every motorist, they are particularly crucial to safe Police Driving Operations. The Driver should always be aware of the limitations to vision and should take steps to counteract these by maintaining high observation skills, developing a keen sense of perception and anticipating how events are likely to unfold.

Chapter 7
Hearing and Communication

Introduction

Next to vision, hearing is the most important sense used by the Police Driver. It provides him with a "sound picture" of his surroundings and outside world, enables him to communicate with other crew members and the Control Room, and can provide him with warning signals from other motorists.

65

Functional Anatomy of the Ear

The functional anatomy of the ear is shown in Figure 7.1 from which it can be seen that there are three major components;—outer, middle and inner portions. The outer ear picks up soundwaves from the environment, and funnels them towards a tight membrane separating the outer and middle portions—the *eardrum*. Soundwaves cause the eardrum to vibrate in sympathy and the vibrations are picked up and amplified by a set of three tiny bones linked together, and known as the *ossicles*. They carry the vibrations across the middle ear into the fluid filled *cochlea*—the hearing organ of the body. The cochlea is shaped in a coil, rather like the shell of a snail, and throughout its length runs a thin membrane called the *basilar membrane*. This is supplied by thousands of tiny nerve fibres which join up to form the cochlear nerve. Changes in pitch and loudness of sounds are sensed by tiny hairs on the basilar membrane through the pressure waves transmitted in the endolymph fluid passing up and down the length of the cochlea. The electrical pulses generated by pressure waves in the fluid are transmitted by the cochlear nerve to the brain. Here the hearing centre detects which part of the cochlea has been stimulated and analyses this, and other data to determine pitch and loudness of the detected sound.

Human Hearing

Humans have a fairly wide range of hearing for pitch although it varies with age and amongst different individuals. There is a similar wide range for loudness and the human ear is able to detect sounds from the faintest whisper to the roar of a jet engine. A small proportion of the sounds produced during speech are at low frequencies and these can be transmitted directly through the skull bones to the inner ear in a process known as bone conduction. The full range of speech,

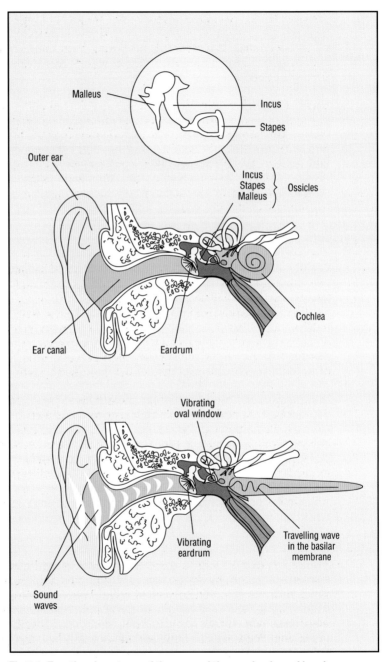

Fig 7.1: Functional anatomy of the ear and the mechanism of hearing

however, lies in the comparatively narrow frequency range of 2,000–5,000 Hz and these sounds are transmitted mainly by the mechanism of air conduction described above. Using both mechanisms, the hearing organs form a tuned system that is particularly responsive to speech frequencies.

Unlike some other animals, man has only a limited ability to locate a source of a sound and he can rarely distinguish between sounds that are less than 45 degrees apart. He manages some crude detection and location through the fact that his two ears are stimulated differently by the same sound. One ear hears the sound very slightly louder and fractionally earlier than the other, and this tiny difference enables the brain to give a rough estimate of the direction from which the sound has come.

Noise Problems

Good hearing is important to the driver, and it should be remembered that the ear is constantly bombarded with unwanted sounds or noise. Noise is a very subjective sensation and a sound which may be agreeable to one person may cause another acute annoyance or even distress. In general we regard noise as an unpleasant, distracting or unwanted sound and although the hearing mechanism is fairly tolerant to noise, its effects on the Police Driver can be such as to make his task more difficult and sometimes less accurate.

Noise may interfere with communications between the occupants of the patrol vehicle and with radio traffic between the control room and the crew. With prolonged exposure it can also act as a stressor that interferes with driving performance and induces fatigue. More seriously, prolonged exposure to high intensity noise may damage hearing and if severe can impair the ability of the police driver to function properly in his work. It is important therefore that he has a knowledge of the sources and extent of noise to which he may be exposed through his occupation.

Sources of Noise

In most workplaces noise is generated both by internal and external sources. In a factory, machines, motors, compressed air, drills and saws are all recognised as rich sources of noise. Even in a comparatively quieter workplace, like an office, noise nuisance can arise from telephones, office machinery, or simply from people walking about and talking. Police vehicle crews and motorcyclists have to operate in high density traffic and other noisy areas in the course of their work. In motorcycle operations, noise emanates from the engine, exhaust system and windrush over the protective helmet. With the requirement to wear close-fitting communication headsets the rider may also be exposed to broad spectrum radio noise. The requirement to patrol slowly in noisy traffic areas, and the use of sirens, can be a significant source of noise in all types of police driving.

Noise can be measured in a variety of ways using different types of noise-meters and is usually expressed in the unit decibel (dB). Table 7A shows some levels of noise measured in areas that might be used by Traffic Patrol Officers.

Source of Noise	Noise Level (dB)
Offices	
Very quiet, small office	40 - 45
Large, quiet office	46 - 52
Large, noisy office	53 - 60
Street Noise	
Main road with through traffic	65 - 75
Moderate traffic	60 - 65
Light traffic - local street	50 - 55

Table 7A: Some typical noise levels in areas used by Traffic Patrol Officers

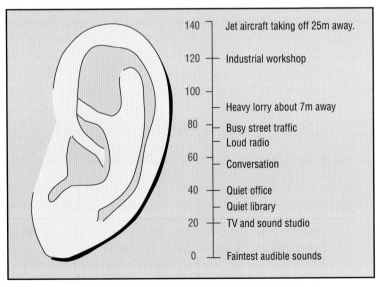

Fig 7.2: Some typical dB(A) noise levels

Fig 7.2 shows some typical noise levels in other working situations. It can be seen that from the faintest audible sound (0 dB) through the noise of a quiet office (40 dB) to the roar of a jet aircraft taking off (140 dB) man can be exposed to a very wide range of noise in the course of his work and leisure activities.

Effects of Noise

Hearing Loss

Reduced hearing acuity is one of the most serious outcomes from repeated exposure to loud noise. At first the loss is temporary and lasts for a variable length of time after exposure. The person is unable to hear distinctly during this temporary deafness phase, but with time he gradually recovers his hearing acuity to previous levels. If noise exposure is continued and frequent, transient hearing loss eventually becomes permanent and the person suffers from the effects of Noise Induced Hearing Loss.

69

This form of noise deafness arises through progressive degeneration of the sound sensitive cells in the ear. The louder the noise and the more often it is repeated, the greater is the damage to hearing. High frequency noises that emanate from a compressed air hose or a whining saw, will damage the higher end of the frequency range of hearing, whereas exposure to lower frequency noises like hammering or banging sounds can damage the corresponding low frequency range of the hearing spectrum.

Sensitivity varies from person to person, and some may lose hearing after only a few months of exposure, whilst others may show their first symptoms after many years of exposure to apparently similar noise levels. At first the person may be unaware of hearing loss but gradually notices the need to turn up the sound volume on television or radio, and realises that parts of conversation are being missed. Continued exposure to noise will cause a progressive hearing loss, and this can become quite disabling when combined with the natural hearing loss (presbyacusis) which comes to most people as part of the ageing process.

Hearing acuity is usually measured by means of the clinical test known as audiometry. Here, pure tones of various frequencies are applied to each ear in turn and the lowest level at which the tone can be heard by the listener is plotted on a graph against its frequency. This graph shows by how much the threshold of hearing has to be raised for each frequency, and it reveals any areas of hearing loss that might be present. A relatively simple test like this can identify noise induced hearing loss at an early stage and before any damage becomes serious.

Effects on Communication

In addition to hearing damage, noise can interfere with radio telephone communication between crew members and the control room. Important information may be lost as a result of excessive background noise or distortion of speech transmission. Experience tells us that the sensitivity of the ear to a particular sound, say a Controller's voice, becomes less and less as surrounding noise increases. This is because the understanding of a message passed by radio depends both on the loudness of the voice and the level of background noise. As long as background noise is at least 10 dB below the level of the speaking voice, the message will be understood. If however the voice is unfamiliar or the information is unexpected by the listener, a difference of 20 dB between voice and background noise may be needed. The poor quality of some communication systems can be overcome by reducing masking noise and improving the clarity of the vocabulary from which the signal is taken. Devices like the use of the phonetic alphabet...Alpha, Bravo, Charlie ...can assist voice and message recognition and are used in some circumstances by those required to pass accurate radio messages in a noisy environment. It is not uncommon for vehicle siren noise to blot out radio signals and effectively destroy communication during a rapid response or fast pursuit.

Impairment of Task Performance

Background noise can reduce concentration, interfere with complex mental activities, slow down the interpretation of information, and subsequently impair the performance of a skilled task. To the Police Driver this represents a potential threat, not only to his driving skills but possibly to the safety of a high speed drive. Unexpected, intermittent high levels of noise are most disturbing to mental work, particularly where the operator requires to be alert throughout the task. Noisy environments can also impair driving performance through the disturbance they bring to normal sleep. The importance of disturbed sleep is dealt with in a separate Chapter but it should be noted at this stage that following a night shift, sleep may be disrupted if the Officer is trying to sleep in high levels of daytime background noise. It prolongs the time taken to get off to sleep, increases the number of waking periods and reduces the amount of deep, refreshing sleep. With curtailment of total sleep time and reduction of quality the Officer may report for duty with a noise induced sleep debt and some of the impairment effects of this may be carried over into the operational driving task.

Protection from Noise

The Police Driver must guard against noise both at home and on duty, and must understand the ways in which it can affect the quality of his work. He must also protect his hearing from the less obvious sources of noise that arise from recreational activities, like discotheques, use of personal stereos, and a variety of sporting activities. He must take every precaution either to avoid exposure to continuous loud noise or reduce the level reaching his ears by the use of personal hearing protection.

Reducing the noise to which operators are exposed at work can be approached in a number of ways. The ideal method is to reduce it at source and this is best addressed as early as possible in the planning and construction stages of the workplace. Choice of noise attenuating building materials as well as the strategic positioning of offices as far from noise sources as possible all help to reduce disturbance to the operator.

Where it is possible a second, commonly adopted, approach is to enclose the source of noise in sound absorbing compartments. Other techniques involve the use of sound-absorbing materials like acoustic tiles on floors and ceilings which can reduce noise by the time it reaches an operator working several metres away.

In some working conditions it is not possible to control or contain noise at source and under such circumstances it may be necessary to resort to some form of personal hearing protection. This can take the form of suitable ear plugs made of synthetic materials which can attenuate noise. Earplugs, however, sometimes impose difficulties for the wearer in that for effective noise attentuation they must be positioned well into the external ear canal and some people find this uncomfortable. A few experience irritation of the skin lining the ear, and are prone to minor ear infections. Some Police Motorcyclists may experience difficulty with the use of earplugs which, although they provide protection, can attenuate auditory input signals coming from the machine upon which may depend driving efficiency. An alternative form of personal hearing protection is through the use of ear-muffs which can achieve very good noise reduction even in high noise fields. They too have minor drawbacks and some wearers find that they are heavy to wear and cause difficulties in person-to-person communication.

Police Motorcylists Helmets

The protective helmet worn by Police Motorcyclists serves several functions, one of which is to protect against noise and provide a platform for communications. It contains a built-in microphone and earphones which are designed to suit Police radio telecommunication even in the noisiest environment. Unfortunately matching imperfections and other distortions external to the helmet may reduce the quality of the message that is actually transmitted and received.

Helmet mounted earphones are carefully chosen so that the signal-to-noise ratio is reduced without the need for the listener to turn up the volume of the receiver to levels which he would find disturbing over long periods of time. By the use of built-in ear-muffs made of sound attenuating materials, and by careful fitting of the shells over the ears, good noise attentuation can usually be achieved. Fortunately in this aspect, most Police communications operate over a frequency band which coincides with the area of reasonably good helmet attentuation and the range of frequencies normally used to convey speech. Although advances are being made constantly to improve communication systems and protect operators against the undesirable effects of noise, it is still important that each individual Traffic Patrol Officer takes great care to preserve his sense of hearing knowing that it is such a vital component of his work.

Chapter 8
Vehicle Motion Effects

Introduction

Police Drivers spend a large proportion of their working time in a Patrol Vehicle which, unlike static work places, may expose them to the effects of vibration. Like every mechanical system, a car possesses the elementary properties of mass and elasticity, and is therefore capable of being set into oscillating motion or vibration. Vibrations set up in the engine, transmission system, or from wheel contact with rough ground, may be transmitted through the seat or via hand and foot controls to the driver's body. Depending on their intensity and frequency characteristics, they can cause disturbance to individual organs, or larger body segments. They do so by exciting oscillatory movements in the part at what is known as the "natural resonant frequency". Movement in the resonating part is amplified many times that of its input oscillation and it is this excessive movement which can cause difficulties in maintaining posture, discomfort and in rare cases, actual damage to organs themselves.

Whole Body Vibration

Fortunately, the body has excellent built-in defences against the damaging effects of vibration through its ability to dampen it down to more acceptable levels before it reaches vulnerable parts. This effect is seen at its most efficient in a person standing on a vibrating platform where the legs effectively reduce the intensity to levels that will not cause harm. Even a seated driver is well equipped to dampen out vehicle oscillations and any that are transmitted through hand controls are usually reduced to about a third of their initial amplitude by the time they reach the elbow. When they reach the shoulder their intensity is further reduced to a tenth of the input value and, as a consequence, vulnerable areas like the head and neck are protected from their harmful effects.

Despite the excellent dampening properties of the human body, the seated driver may be exposed to short-term harmful vibrations when operating over rough terrain. Some vibrations are less well attenuated and although they are likely to be of low intensity and experienced over short periods of time, they can nonetheless add to the driver's difficulties. This is particularly the case if they come on top of other conditions that impair performance. Additionally, vibration and its resonance effects can contribute to postural fatigue and can be a source of annoyance and distraction to a driver attempting to devote all his concentration to an operational task.

Vibration and Health

In the past, attention has tended to focus on the injurious effects of high magnitudes of vibration experienced in off-road and heavy earthmoving vehicles. Disorders have been reported among drivers of heavy plant, tractors and trucks. In these occupations, the commonest adverse effect is muscular pain, although other reported conditions include abdominal discomfort, digestive problems, urinary difficulties, problems of balance, visual disorders, sleep problems and headaches. These conditions are reported much less often in road vehicles although when they do occur they appear to depend to a large extent on the magnitude, frequency, direction and duration of the vibration exposure. Some of the more common vibration effects on the driver are summarised in Figure 8.1.

More recent studies have confirmed that at lower levels, vibrations experienced over comparatively short periods can cause difficulties for Police crews. Back pain is a common problem and it is believed that this condition may be aggravated during periods of poor ride quality when vibrations are induced in the vehicle. Back pain seems

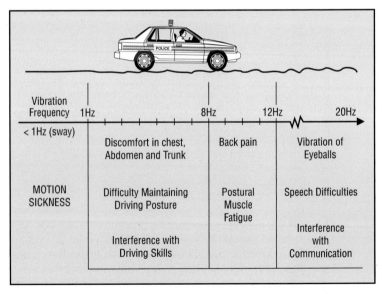

Fig 8.1: Some effects of vehicle vibration

to occur most commonly when the vibration contains a component in the frequency range (8–12 Hz) found in road vehicles operating over rough terrain. Part of the effect may be due to the driver constantly requiring to alter the tension of his back muscles in an attempt to maintain his driving position. This may be additive to the muscle tension of back muscles induced by anxiety and stress during demanding phases of driving. The combined effects of poor ride quality can result in quite disabling back pain in some drivers.

At higher intensities of vibration a driver may experience transient discomfort in the chest, abdomen and trunk and a few complain of difficulties in breathing due to resonance effects set up in the chest. At the critical frequency it is known that the contents of the abdomen move up and down in a piston-like pumping action and this may lead to discomfort. Such severe symptoms are fortunately rare in normal Police driving operations.

Vibration and Driving Performance

Another adverse effect of vibration is the disturbance which it can cause to vision and observation skills. The precise effects depend on the relative movements of the viewer and the scene. Where the object of regard is stationary and the viewer is vibrating, good visual acuity can usually be maintained up to a vibration frequency of 6–8 Hz after which poor vision may occur. Above 50 Hz even mild vibration intensities induce oscillations of the eyeballs in their sockets and the driver may find it difficult to fixate his gaze on the object viewed.

Drivers may also be exposed to vibrations at frequencies which are known to impair efficiency of performance. These are usually encountered at their most severe when driving over rough roads. The adverse effects on driving increases with the intensity and frequency of the vibration (usually around 4 Hz) and in unusual conditions these may reach levels where the number of driving errors becomes so significant that it constitutes an operational risk.

Motion Sickness

Motion sickness is a special response to vehicle motion. It can be experienced by some drivers and passengers of vehicles when they are exposed to unfamiliar motion in the lower frequency range of less than 1 Hz. Some Police drivers may never suffer from the effects of motion sickness and can cope with even the most provocative rides without difficulty. Others may be less fortunate and when subjected to more demanding or anxious-making manoeuvres, experience mild motion sickness effects for the first time. Others may experience a form of motion sickness when they are introduced to the unfamiliar motion environment of a vehicle simulator. Most early sufferers, however, overcome the condition and may be inconvenienced only on the rarest of occasions when other circumstances like unpleasant sights or smells prevail.

Signs and Symptoms

The cardinal signs and symptoms of motion sickness are nausea and vomiting accompanied by palor of the face and sweating. Other responses are occasionally reported but are much less typical. Onset of car sickness follows an orderly sequence, the timescale of events depending largely on the circumstances of the ride and the susceptibility of the occupant. The earliest sensation is one of "stomach awareness" which rapidly develops into intense nausea, followed by cold sweating and excessive salivation. At this stage the victim may show other signs that include frequent belching, yawning and complaint of headaches or drowsiness. The final outcome is the phenomenon known as "avalanche" where the symptoms intensify very rapidly and culminate in actual and sometimes quite severe vomiting.

Cause of Motion Sickness

The cause of motion sickness is not entirely understood. There is common agreement that it arises when information from the eyes, balance organs and other receptors are at variance with the information expected by the brain in the prevailing situation. This mis-match of information is believed to provoke the condition and several aspects of driving are known to create the circumstances where it can appear. These are very variable and individual but can occur when a passenger looks through a side window of a moving vehicle for a long period of time. Looking through binoculars from a moving vehicle can also induce mis-match of information and some people find that reading maps, instruments or other material when a car is moving will rapidly induce symptoms.

Susceptibility to the condition is similarly, very variable and there are wide differences between individuals. Most adults are immune to all but the most provocative circumstances, although a few find that if they move from the driving to the passenger seat of a car they can sometimes experience motion sickness problems. Factors that may play a part in causing motion sickness include anxiety, low levels of residual alcohol in the blood, as well as an overt alcoholic hangover.

Prevention of Motion Sickness

The body has remarkable powers to adapt to new situations and with continued exposure to motion new sensory patterns become accepted by the brain and the balance organs. When this is complete motion sickness happens much less easily. This, perhaps, explains why some susceptible but adapted drivers may experience symptoms of car sickness in the first drive after a break. It possibly occurs because the sensory mechanisms lose their adaptation to motion and a finite time is needed to recover tolerance once again. To prevent this occurring Police Drivers who know that they are susceptible should take the following precautions when returning to duty after a spell of absence:—

77

▶ If in the passenger seat, try and keep spells of instrument, map or document reading to a minimum and maintain forward vision for as long as it is practical and safe to do so.

▶ Although there is little evidence to suggest a relationship between car sickness and ingestion of food, it is sensible to maintain adequate levels of blood sugar by taking regular light meals or snacks.

▶ If you begin to feel nauseated it is often helpful to open a window to relieve stuffiness or expel odours that may be contributing to the problem.

▶ If there is a need to resort to medicines, these should be taken for as short a time as possible and only to allow re-adaptation to take place. Remember the possible side-effects of these medicines which include drowsiness, increased response time, reduced co-ordination and less efficient brain information processing.

▶ If motion sickness becomes a troublesome and frequent occurrence, or re-adaptation to motion after a period of absence from driving is delayed, medical advice should be sought.

Chapter 9
Shifts, Sleep and Driver Fatigue

Introduction

Like many other Organisations, Police Traffic Departments are required to operate on a continuous basis and to do so, employ one of the many variants of the Shift System. Most Traffic Officers experience little difficulty in coping with shift work; a few find that it takes some time to adjust to unusual working hours and in a very small minority the requirement to carry out night duties, affects their well-being and even their health. Those in this latter group report problems arising from disruption of family and social life; and some experience quite marked sleep disturbance through having to work by night and sleep by day. Those affected in this way may also suffer minor gastric symptoms and loss of appetite. A few Officers develop signs of mental fatigue as a result of shiftwork and this may be of concern when they are required to carry out some of the more demanding driving operations.

Body Rhythms

Most of the disturbing affects associated with shift work stem from the requirement to perform activities which are out of synchronization with the normal body rhythms. Those required to operate during night time are at variance with their "body clock" which expects night to be a time of recovery and replacement of the energy used up during the day. Many body functions, like temperature, blood pressure and heart rate are controlled by this body clock and the so-called "circadian rhythm" which it generates is synchronized into a cycle of approximately 24 hours. The various "time-keepers" which maintain body rhythms in synchrony occur in our everyday lives and include change from daylight to darkness, daily social contacts, work schedules and a knowledge of clock time. To the shift worker, the important brain functions driven by circadian rhythm are a readiness for work and the mental abilities to carry out complex tasks. Taken as a whole they gear the body to performing most tasks best by day, and are usually damped down at night to allow recuperation and renewal of reserves.

Organisation of Shift Work

There are many variants of the shift system in operation, and all have their advantages and disadvantages. Most Traffic Departments

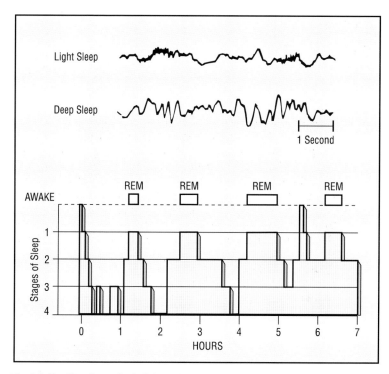

Fig 9.1: Profile of a typical night's sleep

operate a shift system in which the day is divided into three periods of eight hours each—an early, late day and night shift. A few Organisations prefer to operate a two shift system of twelve hours each. No matter which system is utilised, all are carefully designed to provide the most suitable working conditions and least disruption to family and social life. They are similarly chosen to provide opportunities for recuperative sleep, especially during early and late day working.

Each of the shifts in the three shift system has features which inevitably affect the domestic, social life and work of the Traffic Police Officer. The early shift makes a family evening meal possible, although if an early start is required, night sleep may be cut short and tiredness may ensue over the course of the work period. The late day shift is considered by many to be disadvantageous to social life and the pursuance of leisure activities. On the other hand, after a late shift, sleep is usually adequate in duration and of reasonably good quality. By contrast, the night shift is generally considered as the least amenable to social and domestic life with family activities possible only during the evening, and recreational activities confined to the later part of the afternoon. Sleeping habits are often disrupted after night work with problems encountered by the requirement to sleep by day.

Sleep Patterns

The most noticeable function geared up to a day/night body rhythm is that of sleep. The real function of sleep is improperly understood, although it is accepted that it should be undisturbed if it is to maintain efficiency, well-being and even the health of a person. Most people require about eight hours sleep per night, although some would claim to require much less than that and still waken up refreshed and ready for work.

The quality of sleep is not uniform but seems to cycle throughout the sleep period with the sleeper ascending and descending into various stages as shown in Figure 9.1. Each of the stages of sleep is characterised by a particular pattern of electrical waves recorded from the brain—the electroencephalogram (EEG) and this can be used to study the depth and quality of each sleep pattern.

The first stage lasts approximately one to seven minutes and is the time during which the person normally drops off to sleep. It is quickly followed by the second stage which is a period of lighter sleep and the one which occupies about half of our total sleeping time. This is followed by the third stage which is a deeper phase of sleep and leads on to stage 4 which is the deepest sleep phase of all. At certain times during sleep, Rapid Eye Movements (REM) are characteristic and in this phase dreaming is especially common. Paradoxically, although marked activity can be seen in the brain's electrical patterns during REM sleep, it is also a time of maximum relaxation of muscles. In this phase the sleeper strenghthens and organises his memory and learning new tasks often results in an increased proportion of REM sleep.

Day Sleep after Night Shifts

Many of the sleep problems which Traffic Police Officers encounter after a period of night duty relate to disturbance of natural body rhythm (Figure 9.2). Difficulty in getting off to sleep may be due to background noise which is usually greater in a residential area during daylight hours than at night. The "body clock" is slow to adjust to unusual working and resting cycles so that those involved in certain shifts feel unrefreshed after the 'abnormal' sleep period. Studies have

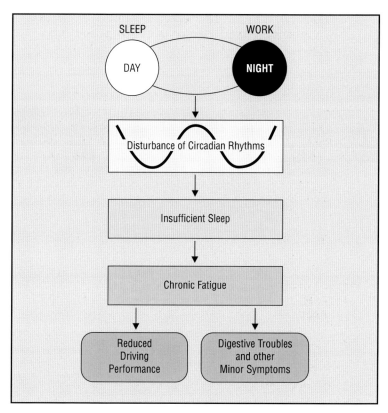

Fig 9.2: Disturbance of natural body rhythm caused by night work

shown that on average, daytime sleep after night duty is distinctly shorter than the normal nightime sleep and averages about six hours. Many build up a mild sleep debt which requires to be repaid on rest days and it usually takes about two of these for the Officer to reach full recovery. The quality of sleep may also be impaired as a result of a greater number of periods of light sleep, with more frequent restless body movements. Overall, the sleep that follows a night shift is curtailed in quantity and quality and more likely to be of less restorative value than the normal nightime sleep.

Other minor problems which accompany sleep disturbance include loss of appetite and minor digestive upsets. These may arise from changes in eating habits which result from the modified routine of a night shift. Problems occur particularly when there is incomplete adjustment to night work and the body system is only partially switched over to the change in routine. There may be other difficulties caused by disruption to family life, interference with social contact and the existence of fewer opportunities to participate in recreation or group activities.

Effects on Mental Processing

Mental processing during performance of a skilled task may suffer as a result of night duties and disturbance to sleep patterns which they can bring. As well as a rhythm for the basic physiological functions previously mentioned, the body clock also regulates daily cycles associated with much more complex behaviour. Tasks requiring fast reaction times, vigilance, observation and visual scanning follow a pattern throughout the working day, and exhibit periods of maximum efficiency followed by troughs where their accuracy is reduced. There is marked individual variation in the times at which peaks and troughs appear and these vary according to the nature of the working patterns. The efficiency of tasks requiring memory declines progressively throughout the day and activities that depend on reasoning seem to peak at around midday with alertness dipping soon after the midday meal. There is a wide individual variation in responses and each Police Driver should try and identify his own individual pattern of peaks and troughs so that he can adjust his work to avoid disturbance as much as possible. It is known that when road traffic accidents occur during the night shift, they peak during the early hours of the morning, a time which is considered to be a driver's lowest phase of circadian efficiency. The Police Driver must be aware of this and overcome the danger by keeping up vigilance and concentration at all times.

Developing Sleeping Habits

About one third of the adult population experiences difficulty either in falling asleep or staying asleep. For those who experience difficulties, it is useful to develop good sleeping habits and some of the following suggestions may assist in dealing with sleep problems.

► Try to go to bed at a pre-determined time after each shift.

► Establish a personal bedtime routine in order to "set the mood to sleep".

► Avoid the temptation to take short naps during rest breaks.

► Avoid bedtime beverages like coffee and tea which contain caffeine and have wakening properties.

► Avoid too much mental stimulation before retiring to bed, since an active mind may prevent getting over to sleep.

▶ Avoid heavy, high fat content meals just before retiring. Digestive processes may delay the onset of sleep.

▶ Make sure that the sleeping quarters are thermally comfortable and are neither too hot nor cold. The room should be well ventilated and, if possible, darkened.

▶ For those who have difficulty getting off to sleep, a warm milk drink or some light reading can be helpful.

▶ Avoid alcohol as a means of assisting sleep. Contrary to popular belief it results in poor quality and unrefreshing sleep and there is always the danger of the presence of residual alcohol in the blood on wakening.

▶ Maintain good physical condition by taking a balanced diet and regular exercise. A physically fit person is much less liable to suffer from sleep difficulties.

▶ Seek medical advice before resorting to sleep promoting drugs (hypnotics).

Mental Fatigue State

It is necessary to differentiate between the state of true mental fatigue which is objective and the feelings of tiredness which are subjective. True fatigue follows a prolonged and mentally demanding drive and is accompanied by changes in certain body functions which include brain processing of information. It is characterised by reduced alertness and vigilance with a slowing of the driver's response to any sudden demand for action. His actions may become careless and he may leave himself open to an accident.

The onset of mental fatigue is signalled by a reduction in alertness. In a long, tiring or mentally demanding shift, it may set in after about four hours, although it often improves towards the end of the shift. A break after three hours driving is useful in allowing recovery to take place, and this assists towards subsequent improvement in driving performance. If, however, the break time is delayed, recovery from fatigue may be much less effective and after nine hours of non-stop driving little or no refreshment occurs from a break of any duration. To allow full recovery and stave off the effects of mental fatigue a rest break should ideally be no less than about twenty minutes. Any shorter than this and subsequent errors in driving will remain high.

Some Police Drivers notice that on successive days of driving duties there may be earlier onset of fatigue if the shift is particularly demanding. This is sometimes found during night duty if the Officer is also suffering from the effects of disturbed daytime sleep. There is evidence that reduced driver alertness and associated mental fatigue at night may be closely related to the occurrence of road traffic accidents.

In the fatigued driver, response times are delayed, vigilance reduced and distracting influences given greater attention. Hazard evaluation is also reduced and decisions and judgements are much less accurate and based on inadequate criteria. He may miss an important demand for some action, fail to notice a hazard, respond too late or engage in an unusually risky manoeuvre. Fortunately Police Drivers have a good insight into the danger of mental fatigue and the impairments which it brings to driving. They are aware that these occur, particularly when the drive is demanding and pressures of work tempt them to continue high performance driving beyond safe limits.

Routine Patrol Fatigue

Recent on-board studies have focussed attention on a particular type of fatigue which can affect the Police Driver. Unlike the more common form of mental fatigue caused by a demanding drive, this state arises when the patrol is monotonous, repetitive and there is little mental stimulation. It typically occurs during night duties and may be aggravated by mild sleep loss and incomplete adaptation by the body clock to change of shift times. When there is little happening, the crew may be exposed to mental underloading and this results in a state close to boredom.

The combination of night driving, low level activity, asynchronous body clock and insufficient mental stimulation is a recipe for the onset of Routine Patrol Fatigue. Symptoms include feelings of weariness, a disinclination for work, sluggish thinking, reduced alertness and poor perception. There is reduced speed of reaction and impaired accuracy of driving performance. In this state, there may be a lapse in distance judgement and a driver may fail to appreciate that the vehicle in front is slowing down until he is suddenly confronted by brake lights. Unlike the more conventional mental fatigue state, the affected driver is usually able to respond quickly if the situation changes and can switch his full attention to the task in hand.

Many Traffic Patrol Officers develop their own strategies to combat Routine Patrol Fatigue, and instead of waiting for something to happen, seek out tasks that broaden and enrich their duties, even if the patrol turns out, at first, to be unstimulating and uneventful.

Avoiding Fatigue

It is important that the Police Driver takes every possible precaution to prevent mental fatigue in operational driving and this may be assisted by the following practical steps:—

▶ Before setting out on patrol, take time to adjust the driving seat to a comfortable position and ensure that all controls can be reached and operated easily.

▶ Ensure that cabin temperature and ventilation controls are set to comfort levels.

▶ Prevent ingress of exhaust and other fumes that may impair performance and hasten the onset of fatigue.

85.

▶ Reduce the level of disturbing windrush and other annoying noises, which add to the problems of fatigue.

▶ Ensure that any meals taken before and during the work shift are light and require minimal digestion. Heavy meals can make the driver sleepy and hasten the onset of true fatigue.

▶ Allow sufficient time for alcohol to clear from the bloodstream before coming on duty. Remember that even small amounts of residual alcohol can lead to drowsiness and impair judgement.

▶ Be careful in the use of medicines remembering that their side effects may induce drowsiness.

▶ Make sure that during a long shift, regular rest breaks are taken. Try and set aside some time to have at least one light meal during the shift.

▶ Be on the look out for the tell-tale signs of fatigue, and spot even minor reductions in normal standards of driving.

▶ In double-manned vehicles always work in partnership and as a member of a team. The passenger can act as a safety factor by assisting the driver with observation.

Chapter 10
The Thermal Environment

Introduction

The Traffic Police Officer may be required to operate in a wide range of working conditions. From the comparative comfort and controlled environment of a patrol vehicle he may be plunged suddenly and with little warning into extremes of climate. He may have to work outside the vehicle in freezing weather where rain, hail, sleet or snow and a biting wind add to the discomfort and difficulty of his tasks. At the other end of the scale he may be required to work under conditions of heat which threaten to raise his deep body temperature and cause excessive heat loading. Although extreme hot weather working conditions are rare in the United Kingdom, police crews may be required to attend a vehicle fire or carry out rescue operations close to an intense heat source.

Even the temperature within the cabin of a patrol vehicle can rise to significantly high levels as a result of solar radiation, combined with metabolic body heat generated by the occupants themselves. Wearing insulating protective garments within a warm cabin or failing to make the correct setting of ventilation and heating controls can all add to the net thermal loading to which the crew may be exposed during a patrol.

To operate safely the Officer must be fully aware of the potential effects of every type of environmental hazard and must know how to take the necessary preventative measures to protect against them. This Chapter aims to create an understanding of the body's responses to various climatic conditions and in particular the way in which heat exchange mechanisms operate to maintain deep body temperature within fine limits. It also provides a knowledge of how changes in the working environment can affect the comfort and efficiency of police operations.

Heat Exchange Mechanisms

Man has the ability to maintain his body temperature within very narrow limits and this allows him to carry out activities within a wide range of thermal conditions. A comfortable person has a deep body or "core" temperature of about 37°C which allows chemical reactions within the brain, heart, liver and other organs to work most efficiently. The body has several mechanisms to ensure that deep body temperature remains constant in conditions where it faces heat loading or overcooling. Heat is gained by the body from internal sources like muscle activity and chemical processes as well as external generators like the sun and other heat sources. To balance the heat gain the body normally loses heat to the air from the exposed surfaces by methods which obey physical laws of conduction, convection and radiation.

Conduction is the method whereby heat moves from a hotter to a cooler object; *Convection* where a draught of air movement carries heat away from the skin surface and *Radiation* where heat is transmitted through the air from the warmer body to a cooler object like a cold wall. Under normal conditions the heat lost from the body by these mechanisms counteracts the heat gained from internal chemical and muscular processes and the body is said to be in "thermal balance".

Keeping Heat Balance

Any change in the temperature of the surroundings or the rate of activity by muscles tends to upset thermal balance and the body brings in several other mechanisms to regulate and restore it under these circumstances (Figure 10.1) The heat control centre is located deep within the brain and constantly receives information about the outside and deep body temperatures. This comes from sensors that are located in the skin or embedded in the major organs.

In *hot conditions* the control centre detects that the body is gaining or producing heat faster than it is losing it and a first mechanism, known as skin vasodilation, is brought into play. Here there is a widening of the blood vessels in the skin which allows more warm blood to flow near the surface and so lose more heat. A second mechanism comes into action if this is not sufficient to restore temperature balance. This is the mechanism of sweating where glands pour fluid onto the skin surface, further assisting heat loss by evaporation.

In *cold conditions* the brain detects that the body is losing heat faster than it can produce it. Heat loss through evaporation by sweat is stopped and it closes down the blood vessels bringing warm blood to the surface. If reduction in heat loss by these methods is still insufficient, the body brings in an emergency mechanism whereby heat is generated by muscular contraction of the limbs—a state which we recognise as shivering.

87

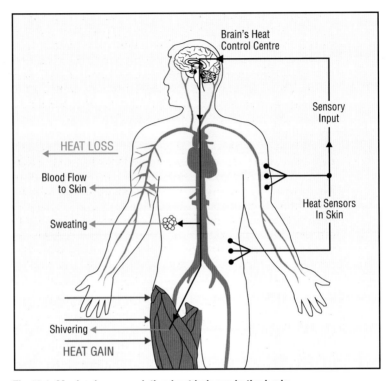

Fig 10.1: Mechanisms regulating heat balance in the body

As a result of these processes the body temperature of an adult does not usually vary by more than 1 C either side of 37 C even when the external temperature changes. Man however, has the ability to assist temperature regulation by applying or discarding items of clothing to suit the external climate. When he faces extremes of temperature he can also take steps to protect himself by wearing special protective clothing assemblies.

Thermal Protective Clothing

Cold/Wet Weather Protection

To operate in foul weather conditions Police Crews should ideally wear a protective clothing assembly that provides thermal insulation, waterproofing and wind resistance yet is lightweight and flexible enough to allow physical activity to be carried out without restriction. It should also provide high visibility through the use of bright material enhanced by reflective tapes that ensure that the Officer can be seen in day and night operations.

The thermal insulating properties of a clothing assembly are mainly due to the thickness of the air layer trapped between the garment and the skin; the fibres themselves contributing little or no insulation property. The usual unit of insulation is the "Clo". Descriptively one "Clo" insulation is that provided by a light uniform or suit with usual underwear. The other unit of insulation which the Reader may come across is the "Tog" now confined to describing the insulating properties of such things as duvets and sleeping bags.

As clothing insulation depends on the poor heat conducting properties of air trapped between the garment and the skin it is vital to keep this air layer as stationary as possible. Effectiveness of insulation can be seriously reduced either by allowing wind penetration to disturb the air layer or by ingress of rainwater which breaks down the thermal barrier. Designers therefore ensure that garments are both windproof and waterproof and this is achieved by using materials like polyurethane coated polyester and ensuring careful positioning of zip fasteners, storm flaps, storm cuffs and seals at the ankles and neck to reduce wind and water penetration.

89

In making a garment waterproof and wind resistant, care must be taken to avoid total water vapour impermeability otherwise normal transpiration of sweat cannot take place. If this occurs there is a build up of moisture which dampens the underclothing and breaks down the heat insulation properties of the garment. Choice of a suitable vapour permeable fabric or the inclusion of "ventile" fabric patches in the garment prevents this from happening. It allows the wearer to sweat freely within the assembly without degrading its thermal protective properties.

A large proportion of body heat is lost from the head and cold weather clothing assemblies should ideally include a storm hood or other suitable headgear. Likewise, gloves prevent heat loss through the hands and help to avoid the danger of "cold burning" of the fingers through contact with intensely cold metal objects. Protection of the feet is also important and assemblies for cold weather operation often include suitable thermal insulating socks and water resistant footwear.

Working in Hot Conditions

Working under very hot climatic conditions is unusual even in the hottest summer in the United Kingdom. On these rare occasions the Officer is normally able to regulate heat balance by discarding layers of clothing, seeking relief from shade or setting up a cooling air flow within the vehicle. If he is required to undertake heavier physical work in warm weather he can usually regulate his heat balance through the normal mechanism of sweating. It is important however that he remembers to replace the fluid and salt lost through sweating. Failure to replace fluid can result in the symptoms of dehydration and this can affect the ability to perform complex tasks and reduce the efficiency of driving.

Care must be taken in the situation where a crew is required to operate in warm weather or close to a heat source whilst wearing bulky, thick, multilayered protective clothing. Many protective assemblies create heat loading problems whether they are simple weather resistant jackets and trousers or the more specialised and specific assemblies needed for fire fighting. All create a thermal barrier and where heat is generated from muscles through physical activity, thermal loading may be quite considerable. Police motorcyclists are vulnerable to heat loading through the requirement to wear leather clothing designed to protect them against cold and the risk of skin abrasions and injury in the event of a fall. Combined with thick gloves, boots and helmets their assemblies may be ideally suited to cold or wet weather riding but may impose unwelcome heat loading in slow moving traffic on a hot day.

Conditions of Extreme Heat

Protection against the extremes of heat may be required when a crew is called to attend a road traffic accident involving a vehicle fire (Figure 10.2). Under these conditions the Officer must be aware of the dangers of excessive heat loading, and of his clothing catching fire or melting. Professional fire fighters are equipped with clothing assemblies that have built in spark and flame-proofing and they also have available various items of specialised equipment like aluminised radiant heat suits and breathing apparatus. Police crews approaching a fire with lesser protection should be aware that whilst their uniforms or apparel may provide some protection against sparks and flame-licking, this is limited. They should also be careful when touching hot objects unless the gloves worn are made of suitable material that prevents skin blistering and injury. They must also ensure that the face and eyes are similarly protected against extreme heat.

The police driver coping with a vehicle fire must guard against inhaling toxic fumes that are the products of combustion. It is also important to remember that the contents of a tanker or other commercial vehicle may burn and give off highly dangerous and even lethal fumes. Detailed requirements of fire-fighting equipment and methods are beyond the scope of this book, but police crews

Fig 10.2: Sources of intense heat

are advised to be very wary of vehicle fires and should become involved only when they are sure that they are not placing themselves in danger. It is more sensible to leave fire-fighting to those who are fully trained and properly equipped to carry it out safely.

Patrol Vehicle Cabin

Cabin Microclimate

Police drivers spend much of their time in a patrol vehicle cabin, and it is important to appreciate that microclimate can affect the accuracy and comfort of driving through changes in temperature, humidity and air flow. Comfort is a very subjective sensation and a driver may hardly notice the internal microclimate of his vehicle as long as it does not become uncomfortable. Discomfort brings about functional body changes that can affect driving. Overheating leads to weariness, reduced performance of complex skills and an increased liability to make errors. On the other hand, overcooling reduces alertness and concentration and similarly affects the performance of some mental tasks. There is a huge individual variation in the conditions which people accept as comfortable and this depends on the clothing that they are wearing, the amount of physical effort which is involved in the task, and other factors like age and the time of day. The main physiological factors which determine whether a person feels thermally comfortable or uncomfortable are as follows:—

► The difference in temperature between the skin and adjacent areas. Most people feel uncomfortable when this exceeds two to three degrees Centigrade in either direction.

► Humidity which can be uncomfortable when unusually high levels are reached. More commonly, low humidity is noticed by symptoms of dry mouth, nose and eyes.

► Air movement is a very significant factor and if it exceeds 0.5 M per second it is felt as an uncomfortable "draught" especially when directed from behind rather than from the front. The feet and neck are sensitive to air flow and even mild draughts in these areas are considered uncomfortable in a seated person. Conversely, low air flow within a vehicle cabin can give rise to feelings of stuffiness and discomfort.

Cabin Air Quality

Pollution of the cabin air can be unpleasant and at times dangerous. Ingress of exhaust fumes containing carbon monoxide can cause headache, even at very low concentrations and if higher, can lead to disturbance of consciousness and eventually death. Ingress of vehicle and industrial emissions include oxides of nitrogen, benzene, sulphur dioxide and smoke particles and they can irritate the mucous membranes of the eyes, nasal passages and lungs in some sensitive individuals.

Pollutants can arise from the human body itself and although water vapour and carbon dioxide exhaled from the breath have no adverse effects, odours and organic gases, even in low concentration can be unpleasant, distasteful and even distracting. Body odours, breath alcohol fumes, stale tobacco smoke can be given off when offenders are being questioned or transported in a police vehicle. These may be difficult to dispel from the vehicle by the usual methods and dealing with an intoxicated offender incurs the risk of leaving the vehicle smelling of vomit or worse.

93

General Advice

The following advice may help to maintain police vehicle crews in a working environment that is both comfortable, pleasant and enhances the performance of their tasks:—

► If a cabin air-conditioning system is available in the patrol vehicle, ensure that it is set to provide maximum comfort.

► Adjust heating and ventilating controls to suit prevailing conditions and keep the microclimate comfortable.

► Be aware of possible sources of air pollutants and either prevent their ingress or dispel those that have accumulated.

► Be prepared for sudden changes in the operating environment and ensure that you are wearing adequate protective clothing to maintain body temperatures at comfort, efficiency and safety levels.

► If required to operate in unusually hot conditions or be physically active whilst wearing thick insulating clothing, ensure that you maintain adequate salt and water intake to counteract loss through sweating.

► Be prepared in an emergency to operate in very hostile working environments that present you with physical, chemical and other hazards. Make sure that you and others involved in the incident are fully protected before entering danger zones and always work within the limits of the protection available to you.

Chapter 11
Vehicle Design and Layout

Introduction

Good driving begins with careful adjustment of the driver's body into a position that provides the most efficient control of his vehicle. Adopting the correct seating posture is important, not only for comfort, but in preventing postural fatigue that can ultimately lead to impaired driving efficiency. Good posture ensures that the driver can reach and operate all primary and secondary controls. Additionally, it allows him to obtain a clear and unobstructed view of the road ahead and the sides and rear of the vehicle. It enables him to see all important dials on the instrument panel and, where necessary, to detect warning lights. In other words, man, his vehicle and the equipment it contains must be compatible with each other. Good design and layout ensures that the task of driving remains accurate and safe at all times.

The achievement of an ideal driving position depends on many factors including the design and layout of the vehicle in relation to the body size of the driver. Police vehicles are usually chosen from standard models and are modified in certain aspects to suit specific operational requirements. They are restricted therefore to the designs that meet the requirements of the general motoring public. The Motor Industry spends a vast amount of time and money in seeking new designs and shapes of vehicles which will not only appeal to the customer but provide him with the handling qualities he desires. More recently the attention of the designer has been drawn towards the importance of ergonomic features. These not only promote safety but have the added bonus of ensuring that the vehicle is designed to suit a wide range of different human body sizes and shapes. This latter feature has proved to be difficult and requires several compromises to be made to meet the requirements of the majority of the population yet cater for the needs of the smaller and the taller driver. Because of these, it is important to create an understanding of the ways in which design features and equipment layout can affect control and operation of Police vehicles.

Geometric Balance

To overcome the difficulties of providing a vehicle to suit a vast range of drivers, it is necessary for the designer to achieve what is known as "Geometric Balance". It can be seen from Figure 11.1

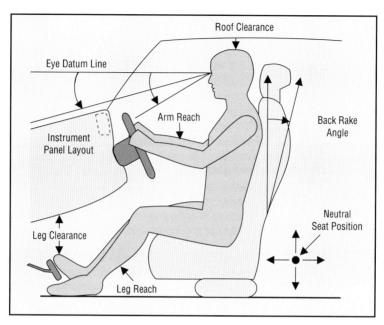

Fig 11.1: Principles of 'Geometric Balance' in vehicle design

that each design feature hinges one upon another and the ultimate objective is to finish up with a design and layout which takes account of all these interactions. The starting point in achieving Geometric Balance is often the "eye-datum line" which is fixed in such a way that the driver can adjust his sitting position to obtain forward view with minimum obstruction allowing good sidewards and rearwards vision. The eye-datum setting immediately dictates the height of the roof line and this must be high enough to give head clearance for even the tallest driver. It also dictates the upper level of the instrument panel so that he can obtain an unobstructed field of view of at least 15° below the horizontal. It similarly determines positioning of the instruments on the dashboard which must be arranged in such a way that the driver can shift his gaze to view them without the need for excessive head and eye movements.

The neutral position of the driving seat should be such that adjustments can be made upwards and downwards and the back of the seat raked to an angle that is comfortable for the driver. It should allow easy access to controls and viewing of essential instruments. These adjustments must again meet the needs of the taller and shorter sitting heights and the sitting position must ensure that there is enough room beneath the dashboard to provide clearance for the driver's legs. The forward and rearward seat adjustments must also cater for drivers with varying arm lengths so that they can reach and operate controls with ease. Similarly the position of foot pedals is determined by leg length in relation to the forward adjustment of the seat.

Matching Controls to the Driver

A major difficulty facing the vehicle designer is the huge variation in body sizes between individuals. It is not enough simply to design the vehicle to suit the average person. Neither is it realistic to aim for a design that will cater for the largest and smallest drivers. We must be content with meeting the requirements of the majority, and the designer makes his calculations on the 2–98 percentile of the driving population. Of practical necessity this must exclude from his consideration the smallest and the largest two percentile.

Important to comfort and safety is positioning of vehicle controls so that they are within reach of the full range of arm and leg lengths as well as other body segments. The height of the steering wheel is a typical example—set it too high and the driver may require to adopt an awkward position of the shoulders that leads to muscle fatigue and cramping pain; too low and he may have to take up a crouched position which will ultimately cause fatigue of the back muscles. To overcome these problems the designer takes account of the full range of every anatomical dimension. He builds in adjustments to the controls wherever possible so that the driver can adopt a comfortable sitting position, have access to all necessary controls and a good view of all important instruments.

In the case of hand and foot operated controls, these must be matched to the natural arc of movement needed to reach and operate them comfortably. Positioning them out of comfortable reach may require excessive trunk movement and this can lead to clumsy, difficult and much less accurate driving. The more frequently used hand controls should be positioned within the natural arc of reach for the average driver, although an occasional stretch to less frequently used controls is considered acceptable (Figure 11.2). Foot pedals need to be positioned so that they can be operated by the full range of leg movements in various planes, (Figure 11.3). Controls that require complex body movements like pulling, pushing and joint rotation need to be placed in the optimum position which allows for ease of operation.

Other human considerations are given to the positioning and style of important instruments. They should provide unrestricted viewing and include the correct colours, shape, illumination and size of

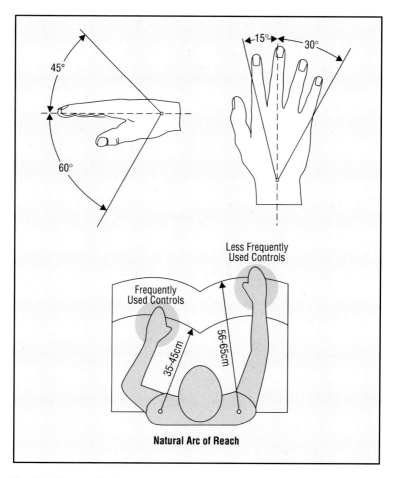

Fig 11.2: Range of limb movements needed for hand-operated controls

numerals that will allow the driver to obtain information from them with ease. Secondary switches and controls that need to be located quickly must be within easy reach and have a separation distance which takes account of the human anatomy and movement range of the fingers.

By carefully matching controls and instruments to the functional and anatomical needs of the driver, the designer can positively enhance driving accuracy and improve safety. By contrast, poor design features and failure of the driver to make use of the available adjustments can lead to discomfort, impaired driving efficiency and, on occasions, medical problems.

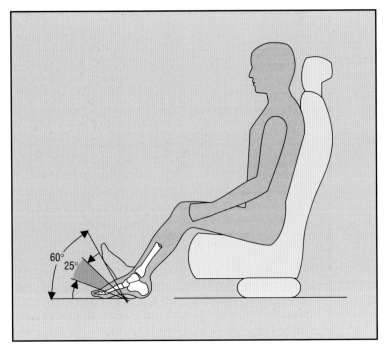

Fig 11.3: Range of operation of legs and feet needed for foot pedal control

To achieve the best features and layout of controls that suit a wide variety of body shapes and sizes, some Manufacturers use a three-dimensional, Interactive Computer Generated Manikin to check the design of their vehicles (Figure 11.4). This "model" has been programmed using a database of limb, trunk and other key body measurements taken from a large sample of the driving population. By programming in different dimensions, the designer can check on the driver's ability to reach and operate controls, highlighting any limbs or joints which are likely to be under strain or liable to be uncomfortable. By running the eye-line across controls he can check that all instruments are unobstructed from view and can be read easily. The model also determines where instruments, knobs and switches should be placed and allows a range of seat adjustments to be chosen which suit drivers of all sizes.

Repetitive Strain Injury (RSI)

Although commoner in other occupations, Repetitive Strain Injury is sometimes reported by drivers. The condition results from repetitious and often inappropriate movements of limb joints and

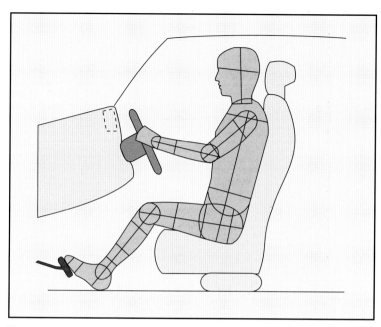

Fig 11.4: Interactive computer generated manikin

muscles that lead to fatigue and ultimately to cumulative muscle strain. It is sometimes described by its alternative name of "Work Related Upper Limb Disorder" (WRULD) a label commonly used to cover a wide variety of soft tissue disorders of the wrists, hands and shoulders. Continuous and excessive gripping of the steering wheel or awkward and repeated movements of the foot and ankle can trigger off the condition whilst bad vehicle design forcing the driver to make overreach and stretching movements can aggravate it.

Despite the name, repetition of movement is only one factor in the disorder, and others include bad sitting posture and a previous history of joint, back or neck problems. It encompasses a whole range of conditions like tenosynovitis, tendonitis or epicondylitis, perhaps more familiar to the reader as "tennis elbow" or "golfers elbow". The main clinical features include pain in muscles, tendons and soft tissues of the limbs. There may be swelling and tenderness and inflammation accompanied by tingling and numbness of the part. If untreated it can lead to functional disability that impairs the movements necessary for driving. It is vital therefore that those, like Police Officers, who depend on a full range of limb and trunk movements for high performance driving should avoid incorrect or awkward body movements which can lead to this painful condition.

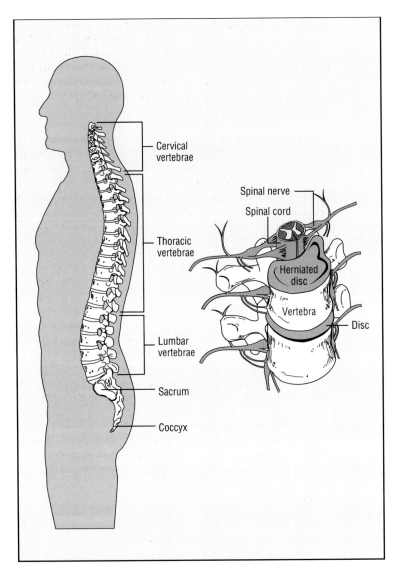

Fig 11.5: Chronic backpain resulting from a 'slipped disc'

Postural Fatigue

Those whose work requires them to be seated in a vehicle for long periods depend on good posture to prevent the onset of lumbosacral strain and occasionally, more disabling lower back pain. A common precursor to back pain is muscular fatigue which follows a long drive particularly where the driver has been forced to adopt an uncomfortable or awkward driving position. The condition is slow in onset but gradually increases in severity as the drive continues. It is due to excessive stretching of microscopic strands of muscles and the tissues that surround them. There may be interference with the blood supply to the tissues and failure to remove all the waste products of muscle contraction causing spasm of the postural muscles.

Back fatigue comes on more readily when the driver is anxious and the muscles of the neck and the back are already in a state of mild tension. It is also commoner in drivers who have spent muscular effort prior to a prolonged drive. Recent surveys of drivers suffering from low back pain and postural fatigue have shown that most fail to adjust their driving seats into a comfortable position before setting off and this emphasises, once again, the importance of establishing a good sitting posture.

101

Lumbosacral Strain

Postural fatigue and discomfort usually disappear after a variable period on leaving the vehicle, but in a few cases the condition fails to recover and pain and restriction of movement persist. This is a feature of true lumbosacral back strain and occurs when overstretching and tearing of muscle fibres and surrounding tissues has been more extensive. The pain and spasm in the back muscles may be so severe as to make movements like bending and stretching exquisitely painful and in extreme cases the sufferer can be totally immobilised. Spasm can be relieved to some extent by the application of local heat and pain can be assisted by taking analgesic medicines. Some longer term relief can result from a course of anti-inflammatory medicine but, with care, recovery, in uncomplicated cases, should be fairly rapid and complete. After the sufferer has made a recovery, care must be taken during the subsequent rehabilitation period to avoid sudden or awkward movements and a return to work too early is a common factor that delays recovery and prolongs the condition.

Chronic Backpain

A few drivers may be unfortunate enough to suffer the more chronic form of backpain which seems to resist all forms of treatment and severely restricts the range of movements which can be performed. One severe form of backache arises through herniation of the intervertebral disc—so called condition of "slipped disc". The intervertebral discs are cushions which separate two vertebrae giving flexibility and shock absorbing properties to the spine (Figure 11.5). They consist of thick, clear viscous fluid enclosed in a tough fibrous ring which may degenerate causing its wall to thin, flatten out and lose its strength. The cushioning properties are reduced and the spine is more prone to damage by a variety of movements that are used in everyday activities. The disc wall may eventually bulge and protrude outside the spinal column, squeezing tissues and nerves and this may cause surrounding muscles to go into painful spasm. When the sciatic nerve, is squeezed by a protruding disc, pain and numbness may extend down one or other of the legs and movements of the back or limbs becomes extremely painful. This condition of "sciatica" can be very difficult to treat and a driver can suffer severe pain with prolonged sitting or by adopting an incorrect sitting posture. Treatment of "slipped disc" and other chronic forms of backpain involves reducing movement of the back and legs by enforced mechanical rest. Pain and spasm of surrounding muscles can sometimes be helped by the application of heat and the use of analgesics and anti-inflammatory drugs. A few cases of chronic backpain respond well to physiotherapy but some more resistant cases may require orthopaedic surgery to correct the condition.

Preventing Backpain

For those drivers who suffer from backpain or are prone to postural fatigue, it is particularly important to adopt the correct sitting position. The aim is to sit with an attitude of the spine that relieves pressure on the muscles and makes longer periods of sitting more comfortable. A good sitting position holds the weight in balance and puts minimum strain on the postural muscles. To assist the ideal posture the angle between the seat and the back rest should be adjustable between 115˚ and 120˚. Additional comfort can be provided by good lumbar support and side supports that prevent swaying movement of the trunk during manoeuvres like cornering.

For all drivers the shape of the seat itself is paramount to sitting comfort and should be wide and deep enough to accommodate the biggest thighs and largest buttocks. A slight hollow in the base helps to stabilise and support the driver and a front edge turned upwards at a slight angle prevents him from sliding forwards. This front edge should be rounded and soft enough to prevent pressure points on the lower surface of the thighs. Opinion is divided amongst drivers as to the comfort offered by soft as opposed to firmer seating and this will always be a matter for individual preference and choice. The main factor to comfort and safety derives from a well-designed seat that gives the full range of adjustment and enables the driver to adopt the driving posture best suited to his own body dimensions.

General Advice

The following measures may assist the driver in obtaining a posture that enhances driving and prevents the onset of discomfort and other medical problems:—

▶ Before setting out on patrol take plenty of time to adjust the seat into a position, with back angle and sitting height which you know to be comfortable and best suited to your driving.

▶ Obtain the driving position and mirror adjustment which provides the optimum view from the vehicle yet allows you to read essential instruments without excessive head movements.

▶ Ensure that all primary controls can be easily reached and operated during the drive.

▶ If involved in heavier than usual physical activity take a break before setting off and allow the postural muscles to relax and recover from their activity.

▶ Take every opportunity for a short break from driving or make a change of driving posture. In double-manned vehicles share periods of driving with a fellow crew member.

▶ If you experience back, neck or leg discomfort stop at the first available opportunity, get out of the car and walk a few times round the vehicle. When you return, take up a new driving position.

▶ Seek medical assistance before back pain or other musculoskeletal conditions become chronic, disabling and interfere with your work.

Chapter 12
Crash Dynamics and Protective Systems

Introduction

Safety in vehicle design has been recognised as important ever since the earliest days of motoring. There are two approaches to car safety known respectively as active and passive measures. Active safety measures are designed to reduce the likelihood of a vehicle being involved in an accident in the first place. They range from features that improve stability, road holding and handling to major developments in braking systems, suspension and tyres. By contrast, passive measures aim to reduce the severity of injuries to the vehicle's occupants where collision is inevitable, and over the years have focused mainly on improving crashworthiness. The fundamental aim in this approach is firstly to ensure that only tolerable deceleration forces reach the occupant's body during a crash, and secondly that the chances of making contact with rigid parts of the vehicle are reduced.

By far the most effective safety measure, however, lies in the hands of the driver himself. With training to high levels of proficiency in driving the chances of an accident can be reduced and with careful adjustment of seat position and correct use of the restraint harness, much of the risk of serious injury can be avoided. It is important therefore that the Traffic Police Officer has a knowledge of the dynamic responses of the human body to a crash situation and understands the need for adjustment and correct use of crash protection devices and equipment.

Deceleration Forces

During a vehicle crash the forces involved are complex and vary both in magnitude and direction. The occupants may be exposed to very abrupt forces of deceleration which, in themselves, can result in injury and even death. The body, however, is amazingly tolerant to deceleration and a driver can survive crash impacts that yield high forces in the chest-to-back direction, provided the pulse of energy is less than 0.1 sec. Forces which take longer to dissipate their energy are much less well tolerated. Although there is still uncertainty concerning human tolerance to abrupt deceleration, crashes are sometimes categorised into "tolerable" where the occupant receives forces that produce some injuries to organs and parts, but which do not usually lead to incapacitation. Forces which are "injurious" produce more severe trauma and in these the injuries may be permanently incapacitating. Those forces which are not normally survivable by the human body arise in very serious accidents where the vehicle and its occupants are subjected to extremely high energy impacts.

The category of force and the nature and extent of the injury which results depend on the peak values of energy which actually reach the seated occupant. This in turn depends on the nature of the vehicle, the weight and structure of the bodywork and the speed and angle at which it hits another object. If the structure crushes and deforms much of the kinetic energy of the crash may be absorbed before it reaches the occupants but if there is little energy absorption and high peak values of deceleration result, the outcome may be more serious. Vehicle designers often use information on crash dynamics in the design of vehicles arranging that structures collapse progressively during an impact and absorb some of the kinetic energy of the crash as they do so.

Crash Injury

Experience of road traffic accidents (Figure 12.1) has provided knowledge of the injuries which can result from various types of impact. Whilst injury and death can result from deceleration forces alone, more often injuries arise from collapse of the cabin structure onto various parts of the body. There can be collapse of the vehicle shell in a roll-over crash or intrusion of large masses, like the engine into the cabin space. Accidents of this type lead to severe and often fatal trauma, and where there is trapping of the occupants death may result when they are unable to escape if the vehicle goes on fire. Injuries can result from objects breaking loose and striking the body and others result from the occupant himself striking internal vehicle structures like the steering wheel or the windscreen.

Analysis of data obtained in experimental crashes using dummies, confirms the dynamics of a severe frontal impact where the vehicle stops in a fraction of a second but the occupants are unable to decelerate and stop as quickly. When the crashing car comes to rest they are still moving forwards at the original speed and if not suitably restrained, will smash into the windscreen, steering wheel or facia. A further problem comes when the impact is so severe that the shell of the passenger compartment collapses reducing the available

105

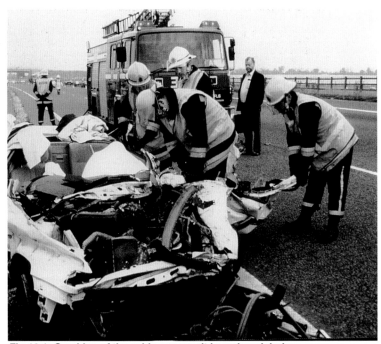

Fig 12.1: Crushing of the cabin can result in serious injuries

space for the occupant to decelerate. In these circumstances the driver's face may hit the steering wheel or windscreen resulting in serious head injuries. The knees can move forward hitting the facia and where energy loading at the knees is transmitted up the leg bones, through the hip joint and into the pelvis, can result in fracture and damage of surrounding tissues and organs. In very severe crashes of this type there may be serious internal bleeding and this may result in loss of life.

Restraint Systems

To prevent the occupants of a crashing vehicle from moving forward and striking objects, it is necessary to provide some form of restraint which holds them firmly in their seats during impact. A seatbelt provides good body restraint during this phase, and if it is made out of suitable material, stretching of the webbing itself can assist in absorbing some of the forward energy. To be effective, the harness must be properly adjusted with as little slack as possible. Some systems incorporate a pre-loaded device that senses crash deceleration forces and takes up slack in a matter of milliseconds.

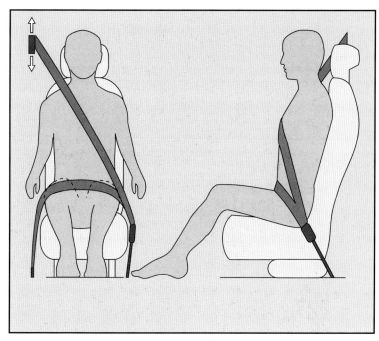

107

Fig 12.2: Three-point harness system

As part of the effectiveness of a seat belt lies in the stretching of the webbing material and absorption of energy, this mechanism can only be effective once and after a vehicle impact the seat harnesses should always be replaced.

A commonly used restraint is the "three-point harness system" shown in Figure 12.2. It consists of diagonal and lap straps which, give excellent restraint in a crash. It prevents the occupant impacting on vehicle structures even in crashes that produce very high levels of deceleration in the fore-and-aft direction. It does however have some minor disadvantages in that if it is not correctly adjusted the lap belt can rise off the pelvis during impact and transmit forces through the abdominal wall, squeezing some of the internal organs. This danger can be overcome by correct positioning and adjustment of the harness. Another inevitable disadvantage is that the legs are not restrained and are left free to be thrown forward and upwards in an impact, often striking the underside of the instrument panel. These may be considered as comparatively minor penalties to pay for a system of restraint which increases the chances of survival in an otherwise fatal crash. It does, however, emphasise the importance of making the correct adjustments to the harness restraint system to enable it to work properly and efficiently in an emergency.

The design features of a good harness restraint system are summarised as follows:—

▶ It should keep the vehicle occupant in his seat during a wide range of sudden decelerations encountered in a crash.

▶ It should be made of webbing or other material that helps to spread the forces and absorb energy over as wide an area of the body as possible.

▶ It should be adjustable so that it does not cause fractures of the skeleton, or cause injury to other internal organs during impact activation.

▶ It should be comfortable to wear, easy to don and easily released in an emergency escape situation.

▶ It should be adjustable over the full range of body sizes of the driver and passengers.

▶ It must provide adequate restraint against displacement of the body by forces coming in from different directions during impact.

▶ It should allow the driver sufficient freedom to reach and operate all controls and give unrestricted ability to perform every driving task.

Medical Exemption from wearing Seat Belts

The law allows exemption from seatbelt wearing on medical grounds and Traffic Police Officers may come across motorists who hold temporary, though rarely permanent, Certificates of Exemption. Many applicants for exemption are unnecessarily worried about the effects which wearing a seatbelt might have on their disability or medical condition. Some reasons put forward include aggravation of existing arthritis of neck and shoulders, irritation of chest and abdominal scars or adverse pressure effects on female breasts. There is no evidence to suggest that these fears are founded and most sufferers can tolerate properly adjusted seatbelts or apply soft padding over sensitive or tender areas to reduce the problem. Similarly, obesity and pregnancy are no longer considered as valid reasons for exemption. Most registered disabled drivers can wear seatbelts without undue discomfort and a few who experience difficulties can usually be assisted by the use of appropriate devices or slight modification to the system.

Airbag Systems

Combined with an efficient harness restraint system, an airbag offers the occupant additional protection against impact with cabin structures. It consists of a strong inflatable neoprene coated woven nylon bag stowed in a convenient position. It is inflated by compressed gas contained in a cylinder and is triggered into operation by a device sensitive to rapid deceleration. When triggered off, gas inflates the bag, usually within forty milliseconds of impact, so that the driver's face is cushioned from the steering wheel.

Most bags contain porous panels that allow air to leak out slowly so that the occupant does not remain immobilised and trapped in the event of fire. To prevent forward and downward movement of the body—so called "submarining"—well designed airbags ensure that the legs, knees and the torso are also protected against forward impact. Side-mounted airbags are less common but, where fitted, they help to prevent impact with side structures during sideways crashes.

109

There have been several disturbing reports from the USA that one version of the Airbag System can cause serious injury and several deaths have resulted from rapid inflation at low impact speeds (5 mph). Airbags used in the UK are usually much smaller in size and inflation is triggered off at much higher impact speeds (19 mph). These are far less likely to cause injury and have saved countless lives in serious vehicle crashes.

Although a variety of experimental crash protection systems are constantly under review, experience has shown that a well adjusted conventional seat harness, combined with an effective airbag system, will provide a high level of lifesaving protection in the event of a vehicle crash.

Head Restraint

Provision of a suitable head restraint is important in guarding against whiplash injury—one of the most common results of a rear impact collision. In such a collision the vehicle is suddenly accelerated forwards with the result that the driver's head is snapped backwards over the seat back. Whiplash injury occurs in this situation and in its slightest form, may result in pain and spasm of the neck muscles. In its more serious form, it can cause chronic neck injury requiring more sophisticated treatment and sometimes months of pain and restriction of physical activities. A head restraint can prevent damaging whiplash head movements although, like seatbelts and other protective devices, it must be correctly positioned. It should be adjusted so that the centre of the headrest cushion meets the bony prominence at the back of the head (occiput). Failure to make the correct adjustment renders the protective device useless and may actually compound the neck injury in a rear impact collision.

Head Injury

Head injury is common in all forms of accident trauma and accounts for a high proportion of fatalities in Road Traffic Accidents. A number of injuries arise when the head strikes a hard object, or conversely when an object strikes the head. Much of the energy of impact to the head is absorbed by the skull bones which break up in a characteristic shatter pattern spreading from the outer surface of the skull inwards towards the brain itself. Energy of the blow that is not absorbed by this fracturing process can travel onwards and injure the brain and its covering membranes. When blood vessels are torn blood accumulates in the skull cavity and after a latent period, the victim lapses into unconsciousness as pressure builds up in the skull. Emergency medical treatment and surgery may be needed to stop the bleeding and relieve the pressure of the accumulated blood on the brain tissue. Delay can result in a fatal outcome in this type of injury.

More complex brain injuries follow absorption of force of impact when the head is either displaced suddenly or brought to a sudden stop during impact. Angular acceleration causes shear forces to develop within the brain causing local and often widespread damage. The brain stem as it enters the spinal cord is very vulnerable to damage of this type, and where there is shearing of membranes and tearing of blood vessels intracranial bleeding may follow. Very serious and often fatal head injuries arise from this type of head displacement injury.

A less severe and fairly common head injury can result in the clinical state of concussion. This is a transient phenomenon of variable duration characterised by widespread symptoms of a paralytic kind   There is rarely permanent damage to brain tissue and it causes no long term residual effects although the victim may have a period of amnesia about events before and for some time after the accident.

Preventing Head Injury

The problem of preventing head injury on impact may be approached in a number of ways. Restraint harnesses and airbags prevent contact of the head with surrounding structures. Provision of adequate space in the cabin within the occupant's immediate environment also helps to reduce injury associated with flailing of the head and contact with surroundings. It is also possible sometimes to treat the surfaces of hazardous areas in a vehicle cabin in order to minimise injury. Projections can be constructed of deformable material padded out to allow cushioning of a blow and absorption of energy when the head strikes it.

111

Care should be taken in the securing and stowage of every piece of equipment in the rear seat of the vehicle to prevent it from being thrown forward in a crash and striking the head of a front seat occupant.

Protective Helmets

In the protection of Police motorcyclists there is no alternative but to resort to personal head protection in the form of a safety helmet. These vary widely in design and shape and different models are used by Police Forces throughout the United Kingdom. All, however, incorporate one or more of the principles of head protection against impact forces which can occur during a motorcyle accident.

A good protective helmet should distribute the impact load over a wide area so as to reduce concentration of force and local tissue damage. It should also prevent deformation of the skull on impact and increase the tolerance to linear acceleration to high levels. The helmet should also provide a finite stopping distance to reduce the peak acceleration in a crash impact. In practice, energy absorbing systems are used to allow a stopping distance between the head and the inner surface of the helmet. Some helmets favour the use of layers of specialised foam material beneath the helmet shell which crush on impact to about 40% of their initial thickness. Some have double layers of padding using an outer harder layer for energy absorption in high energy impacts and a softer more yielding inner layer which provides comfort and protection against lesser impacts.

No matter which system is employed motorcyle helmets must meet British Standard Specifications and are tested to ensure that they provide the best practicable protection to the motorcyclist at risk. Tests include resistance of the helmet shell to penetration by sharp objects and its ability to provide adequate shock absorption qualities in the event of head impact.

As with other items of protective equipment Police motorcycle helmets should be correctly fitted and comfortable to wear over long periods. They should give minimum restriction to vision, good stability and should not impair efficiency with which the wearer can perform his duties on and off his motorcyle.

Concluding Remarks

This final chapter has touched on some of the tragic consequences which can follow a serious road traffic accident. They serve to remind us that driving, although a necessary activity in modern society, is nonetheless one which is alien to man's usual environment. Those who engage in it are at risk from hazards of mechanical and human failure.

Many years of engineering research into actual and experimental crashes have helped to reduce the risk of accidents which result from mechanical defects. Many of the data thus obtained have been used to set criteria and establish standards for vehicle designers to meet.

Likewise studies of the human physical and psychological processes which interact within the driving task have yielded information which has been used to improve risk management and reduce the chances of a road traffic accident occurring. They have also enabled us to structure training programmes that prepare the Police Driver for even the most demanding and, at times, dangerous drives.

It is hoped that the information given in this book will have created in the Reader a greater understanding of these human aspects and performance limitations which play such an important role in the efficiency and ultimately the safety of Police Driving operations.